OCR
BIOLOGY 2

A-Level Year 2/AL

MODEL ANSWERS

This model answer booklet is a companion publication to provide answers for the activities in the OCR Biology 2 Student Workbook. These answers have been produced as a separate publication to keep the cost of the workbook itself to a minimum. All answers to set questions are provided, but chapter reviews are the student's own and no model answer is set. Working and explanatory notes have been provided where clarification of the answer is appropriate.

ISBN 978-1-927309-16-2

Copyright © 2015 Richard Allan
Published by BIOZONE International Ltd
Fifth printing

Additional copies of this Model Answers book may be purchased directly from the publisher.

BIOZONE Learning Media (UK) Ltd.

Telephone local:	01283 530 366
Telephone international:	+44 1283 530 366
Fax local:	01283 831 900
Fax international:	+44 1283 831 900
Email:	sales@biozone.co.uk

www.**BIOZONE**.co.uk

CONTENTS OCR BIOLOGY 2

CONTENTS OCR BIOLOGY 2

CONTENTS OCR BIOLOGY 2

Cloning and Biotechnology

Ecosystems

Populations and Sustainability

1. Homeostasis (page 5)

1. Homeostasis is the relatively constant internal state of an organism, even when the external environment is changing.

2. (a) Detects a change in the environment and sends a message (electrical impulse) to the control centre.
   (b) Receives messages send from the receptor, processes the sensory input and coordinates an appropriate response by sending a message to an effector.
   (c) Responds to the message from the control centre and brings about the appropriate response, e.g. muscle contraction or secretion from a gland.

2. Maintaining Homeostasis (page 6)

1. Two mechanisms operating to restore homeostasis after infection (a and b any two of):
   • Immune system response with the production of antibodies against the antigens of the pathogen (humoral response).
   • Immune system response with the production of T cells which recognise the antigens of the pathogen and destroy them directly (cell-mediated response).
   • Local inflammatory response (redness, pain, swelling, heat) at the site of infection.
   • Fever (widespread increase in body temperature).
   • The production of antimicrobial substances such as interferon and interleukin-1.
   • Phagocytosis of pathogen by white blood cells.
   All the above aim to destroy the pathogen and/or its toxins and assist a return to homeostasis.

2. Two mechanisms by which responses to stimuli are brought about and coordinated (a and b in any order):
   (a) Hormonal response to stimuli: endocrine glands respond to a stimulus (e.g. a nerve impulse or another hormone or metabolite) by producing hormones which bring about an appropriate physiological response.
   (b) Nervous response to stimuli: direct stimulation of nerves from a sensory receptor causes a reaction to the stimulus. This may be a response requiring interpretation of the message by the brain or it may be a reflex.

3. Two ways in which water and ion balance are maintained, and the organs and hormones involved:
   (a) Water and ions are taken in with food and drink, helping to replace that lost through urine, faeces, and sweat. The digestive organs and digestive hormones are all involved in digestion and absorption processes.
   (b) The kidneys are the primary regulator of fluid and ions. When large quantities of fluid must be excreted, the kidney produces large amounts of dilute urine. When water must be conserved, small amounts of concentrated urine are produced. ADH (antidiuretic hormone) causes more water to be reabsorbed from the kidney (concentrating the urine). ADH secretion increases when blood volume is low. Essential ions (and glucose) are retained by active reabsorption from the kidney tubules. Another hormone, aldosterone from the adrenal glands, increases the absorption of Na^+ ions.

4. Two ways in which the body regulates its respiratory gases during exercise:
   (a) Increasing the rate of breathing. This increases both the rate of oxygen entering the lungs and the rate at which CO_2 leaves. It also increases the rate of loading and unloading of oxygen and CO_2 into and out of the blood.
   (b) Increasing the heart rate. This increases blood flow, which facilitates the loading and unloading of oxygen and CO_2 into and out of the blood. It also increases the speed of delivery of oxygen to working tissues (e.g. muscles) and speeds up the removal of CO_2 and other products of metabolism.

3. Cell Signalling (page 8)

1. (a) **Endocrine signalling** involves a hormone being carried in the blood between the endocrine gland/organ where it is produced to target cells.
   (b) **Paracrine signalling** involves cell signalling molecules being released to act on target cells in the immediate vicinity, e.g. at synapses or between cells during development.
   (c) **Autocrine signalling** involves cells producing and reacting to their own signals (e.g. growth factors from T cells stimulate production of more T cells).

2. The three signalling types all have in common some kind of chemical messenger or signal molecule (ligand) and a receptor molecule (on the target cells, which may or may not be on the cell producing the signal).

4. Negative Feedback (page 9)

1. Negative feedback mechanisms are self-correcting (the response counteracts changes away from a set point) so that fluctuations are reduced. This stabilises physiological systems against excessive change and maintains a steady state.

2. (a) A: Eating or food entering the stomach.
      B: Emptying of stomach contents.
   (b) The smooth muscles in the stomach wall.
   (c) An empty stomach.

5. Positive Feedback (page 10)

1. (a) Positive feedback has a role in amplifying a physiological process to bring about a particular response. Examples include (1) elevation in body temperature (fever) to accelerate protective immune responses, (2) positive feedback between oestrogen and LH to leading to an LH surge and ovulation, (3) positive feedback between oxytocin and uterine contractions: oxytocin causes uterine contraction and stretching of the cervix, which causes more release of oxytocin and so on until the delivery of the infant, (4) positive feedback in fruit ripening where ethylene accelerates ripening of nearby fruit.
   (b) Positive feedback is inherently unstable because it causes an escalation in the physiological response, pushing it outside the tolerable physiological range. Compare this with negative feedback, which is self correcting and causes the system to return to the steady state.
   (c) Positive feedback loops are normally ended by a resolution of situation causing the initial stimulation. For example, the positive feedback loop between oestrogen and LH leading to ovulation is initiated by high oestrogen levels and ended when these fall quickly after ovulation, prompting a resumption of negative feedback mechanisms. In childbirth, once the infant is delivered, the stretching of the cervix ceases and so too does the stimulation for more oxytocin release.
   (d) When positive feedback continues unchecked, it can lead to physiological collapse. One example includes unresolved fever. If an infection is not brought under control (e.g. by the body's immune system mechanisms or medical intervention), body temperature will continue to rise and can lead to seizures, neurological damage, and death.

6. Endothermy vs Ectothermy (page 11)

1. Ectotherms depend on the environment for their heat. Endotherms generate heat from their internal metabolism.

2. (a) The lizard (ectotherm)
   (b) By basking in the sun (to heat up) and retreating to shade (to cool down).
   (c) Eating and exercise cause a rise in body temperature.
   (d) Sleeping generally causes the reduction of body temperature.

3. (a) Allowing body temperature to fall saves energy because the animal does not have to maintain body temperature against environmental variation.
   (b) Ectothermy saves energy because ectotherms are not physiologically committed to maintaining a high metabolic rate. Lower metabolic rates are advantageous when food supplies are low (less energy is required for maintenance).

4. (a) Raising body temperature quickly is important as it allows activity, e.g. for hunting or escaping danger. It also increases the rate and efficiency of metabolic processes

such as digestion.
(b) Panting causes evaporative cooling and helps to keep the temperature of the brain lower than the rest of the body.

5. (a) Optimum temperature range for an endotherm is from 18° or 19°C to 36°C. Between these temperatures, oxygen consumption, and therefore energy expenditure, is lowest.
    (b) Below 15°C more energy is required to maintain body temperature against heat loss. Above 35°C, more energy is used to dissipate excess heat.
    (c) Warming the body, e.g. by shivering, requires muscle movement. Panting requires muscle movement. Cooling by sweating uses cellular energy because secretion (of sweat) is an active process.

---

7. Mechanisms of Thermoregulation (page 13)
1. (a) Behavioural
    (b) Physiological
    (c) Physiological
    (d) Behavioural
    (e) Structural

2. (a) Thick hair reduces heat loss by trapping an insulating layer of air between the animal and the cooler environment. The insulating layer of hair also reduces heat gain from the environment.
    (b) Different fur thicknesses allow an animal to expose or cover thinner areas to allow for greater of lower heat loss depending on needs.
    (c) Related species at low altitude could be expected to have less thick and less dense fur covering than animals at high altitude.
    (d) They have thick blubber and are usually large.

3. In warmer waters, blood is allowed to flow above the blubber layer, letting heat dissipate into the water.

4. Use of countercurrent heat exchange in marine mammals means most of the heat in the blood moving towards the skin of the extremity is transferred to the blood moving away from the skin of the extremity before the blood reaches the coldest part of the body. Therefore the blood is already cooler by the time it reaches the coldest part of the body and no heat is lost to the environment and the blood is warmed again before returning to the body's core.

---

8. Thermoregulation (page 15)
1. Body temperature reduced by ((a) and (b) any two of):
    • Sweating (cooling by evaporation) • Reducing activity (reduces metabolic rate) • Behavioural mechanisms such as removing clothing or seeking shade • Increasing blood flow to skin (leads to increased radiation from the skin surface).

2. (a) Hypothalamus: Monitors temperature changes in the body and coordinates appropriate responses to counteract the changes.
    (b) Skin: Detects changes in skin temperature and relays the information to the hypothalamus. In response to input from the hypothalamus, muscles and capillaries in the skin act as effectors to bring about an appropriate thermoregulatory response.
    (c) Nervous input to effectors (from hypothalamus): Brings about (through stimulation of muscles) an appropriate thermoregulatory response (e.g. raising hairs, constricting blood vessels).
    (d) Hormones: Mediate a change in metabolic rate through their general action on body cells (adrenaline and thyroxine increase metabolic rate).

3. (a) Sweating cools the body by using heat energy transported from the body's core to the skin to evaporate the sweat.
    (b) Methanol and ethanol both have very low temperatures of vaporisation. They feel cold because they absorb heat energy easily and vaporise quickly, rapidly removing heat energy from the skin.

4. Sensory receptors in the skin detect changes in temperature and send signals to the hypothalamus which initiates responses to counteract the changes. Restoration of the normal body temperature leads to reduced sensory output

and the responses are switched off (negative feedback).

5. Blood vessels can constrict (reduce blood flow) or dilate (increase blood flow) to regulate the amount of blood flowing from the body to the skin and back. This regulates temperature by regulating the amount of heat moving from the body's core to the skin's surface where heat is lost.

6. (a) Subcutaneous fat helps to insulate the body and reduce heat loss to the environment.
    (b) Excessive fat does not allow heat to be dissipated easily, making the body more likely to overheat during exercise.

---

9. Chapter Review (page 17)
No model answer. Summary is the student's own.

---

10. Key Terms: Did You Get It?(page 18)
1. ectotherm (I), effector (D), endocrine signalling (C), endotherm (L), homeostasis (A), negative feedback (F), paracrine signalling (E), positive feedback (J), receptor (H), response (B), stimulus (K), thermoregulation (G).

2. A: Type of mechanism: Positive feedback
    Mode of action: Escalation (increase) of the physiological response away from the steady state condition. Once the outcome is achieved, the positive feedback ends.
    Biological example: Fruit ripening, fever, labour, blood clotting.

    B: Type of mechanism: Negative feedback
    Mode of action: Has a stabilising effect, maintains a steady state by counteracting variations from the normal set point.
    Biological example: Regulation of body temperature, blood glucose, and blood pressure.

---

11. Waste Products in Humans (page 20)
1. Excretion enables the toxic by-products of metabolism (CO_2, nitrogenous wastes, excess ions) as well as drugs and poisons to be removed before they can disrupt functioning of organ systems.

2. **Carbon dioxide**: Origin: All metabolising cells.
    Organ of excretion: Lungs.
    Water: Origin: All metabolising cells.
    Organs of excretion: Lungs, kidneys, gut, skin.
    Bile pigments: Origin: Breakdown of haemoglobin in liver.
    Organ of excretion: Gut. The breakdown product passes out in the faeces.
    Urea: Origin: Produced in the liver from ammonia (resulting after breakdown of amino and nucleic acids). Organs of excretion: Kidneys, skin.
    Ions: Origin: General result of cellular metabolism. Organs of excretion: Kidneys, skin, gut.
    Hormones: Origin: Endocrine organs, sometimes ingested (synthetic hormones and anti-inflammatories). Organs of excretion: Kidneys, skin.
    Poisons: Origin: Ingested or inhaled from external sources.
    Organs of excretion: Kidneys.
    Drugs: Origin: Ingested or inhaled from external sources.
    Organs of excretion: Kidneys.

3. The liver produces urea from ammonia (urea cycle) and bile pigments from the breakdown of haemoglobin.

4. – Problems with fluid retention: oedema and retention of fluids containing toxins and waste products.
    – Problems with salt retention leading to hypertension and heart problems as the heart works harder to move the blood through constricted vessels.
    – Problems with the retention of ions other than sodium leading to the toxic effects of high ion levels.
    – Poisoning of the body with its own metabolic wastes eventually leads to coma and death.

© 2015 **BIOZONE** International
ISBN: 978-1-927309-16-2
Photocopying Prohibited

12. The Structure and Role of the Liver (page 21)
1. Hepatocytes

2. (a) Vascular functions (one of):
   Manufactures heparin and blood proteins.
   Acts as a reservoir of blood, being able to store and release blood as required to maintain blood volume.
   (b) Metabolic functions (one of):
   Central to the metabolism of amino acids (e.g. deamination), fats (gluconeogenesis), and carbohydrates (e.g. glycogenolysis, glycogenesis). Synthesises cholesterol.
   Stores minerals and vitamins.
   Detoxifies poisons.
   (c) Digestive function: Secretes biles for the emulsification of fats.
   (d) Excretory functions (one of):
   Produces urea from amino acids for excretion of nitrogen
   Excretes hormones
   Metabolises haemoglobin which is excreted in the bile.
   (e) Storage functions (one of):
   Stores blood
   Stores iron, copper, and vitamins (A, D, E, K, B_{12}).

3. The lobule

13. The Histology of the Liver (page 22)
1. (a) **Supply 1**: Branches of the hepatic artery. **Purpose**: Supply of oxygen and nutrients to the liver tissue.
   (b) **Supply 2**: Hepatic portal vein. **Purpose**: Brings nutrient-rich blood to the liver for processing by the liver cells.

2. (a) **Bile canaliculi**: Carry the bile (secreted by the hepatocytes) to the bile ductules where it then flows into the bile duct.
   (b) **Phagocytic Kupffer cells**: Engulf microbes and break down spent red blood cells.
   (c) **Central vein**: Carries blood (mix of hepatic portal and arterial blood) that has passed through the liver lobule to the hepatic vein (which exits the liver).
   (d) **Sinusoids**: Blood spaces that carry the mix of hepatic portal and arterial blood through the lobules, for processing, and supply of oxygen and nutrients.

3. Venous supply through the hepatic portal system provides a supply of nutrient-rich blood from the gut directly to the liver for processing.

4. The liver is richly vascularised with a system of capillary-like sinusoids ramifying throughout. At any one time, more than half of the 10-20% of liver's volume is in the sinusoids.

5. Sinusoids are leakier than capillaries so small and medium sized proteins can easily leave and enter the blood. This facilitates exchanges between the blood and the hepatocytes.

14. The Liver's Role in Protein Metabolism (page 23)
1. Aspects of protein metabolism (a-c in any order):
   (a) Transamination of amino acids to create new, non-essential amino acids.
   (b) Deamination of excess amino acids and production of urea in the urea cycle.
   (c) Synthesis of plasma proteins.

2. Deamination produces keto acids and an amino group. The keto acids feed into the Krebs cycle and are oxidised to yield ATP. NH_2 is converted to ammonia (toxic) and joins with CO_2 and enters the orninthine cycle to produce urea.

3. Symptoms would be a build up of ammonia in the tissues and, unless addressed by management of diet to minimise protein content, it would be fatal.

15. The Urinary System (page 24)
1. (a) Kidney: produces urine and regulates blood volume.
   (b) Ureters: convey urine to the bladder
   (c) Bladder: stores urine
   (d) Urethra: conveys urine to the outside
   (e) Renal artery: carries blood from aorta to kidney. Supplies the kidney with blood carrying oxygen and urea.
   (f) Renal vein: carries blood from kidney to vena cava.

Returns blood from the kidney to the venous circulation.
   (g) Renal capsule: covers the kidney and protects it against trauma and infection.

2. 99.4%

3. (a) A nephron is the selective filtering element in the kidney. It is the functional unit of the kidney.
   (b) The nephron produces a filtrate from the blood, modifies the filtrate and produces the final excretory fluid (urine).

4. (a) Transitional epithelium is found in the bladder.
   (b) It means the walls of the bladder can be stretched without the outer cells breaking apart from one another.

5. The sphincter allows the voluntary voiding of urine (urination or micturition).

16. Drawing the Kidney (page 26)
Task 1: Student's own drawing.

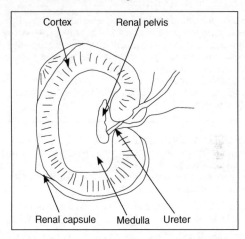

Task 2: Student's own drawing. Points to note:
   – Cells should be drawn with unbroken lines and not overlapping.
   – Cell borders may sometimes be inferred from the positions of the nuclei.
   – Structures to label include tubule lumen, cuboidal cells lining tubules, Bowman's capsule, squamous epithelium lining capsule, lumen of capsule.

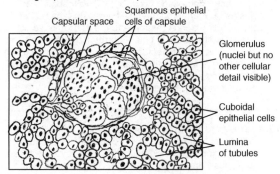

17. The Physiology of the Kidney (page 27)
1. The high blood pressure is needed for ultrafiltration, i.e. to force small molecules such as water, glucose, amino acids, sodium chloride and urea through the capillaries of the glomerulus and the basement membrane and epithelium of Bowman's capsule.

2. (a) Glomerular filtration: Produces an initial filtrate of the blood that is similar in composition to blood and can be modified to produce the final urine.
   (b) Active secretion: Secretion allows the body to get rid of unwanted substances into the urine.
   Explanatory detail: Active secretion of chloride in the ascending limb (with sodium following passively) contributes to the maintenance of the salt gradient in the extracellular fluid (this gradient allows water to be

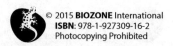

reabsorbed in the collecting duct). Secretion of toxins and unwanted ions into the filtrate in the distal tubules allows the blood composition to be adjusted and poisons to be excreted. Energy is used to secrete these substances against their concentration gradients

(c) Reabsorption: Essential process that allows the useful substances (required by the body) to be retained from the filtrate (particularly the initial filtrate, where 90% is reabsorbed). The body would waste energy if these substances were not retained.

(d) Osmosis: Osmotic loss of water allows the urine to be concentrated (via loss of water).
Explanatory detail: Osmosis is important in two regions of the nephron: In the descending limb of the loop of Henle, osmotic loss of water concentrates the filtrate so that salt can be withdrawn from the ascending limb to contribute to the salt gradient in the extracellular fluid. In the collecting duct, loss of water by osmosis provides the final concentration of the urine

3. (a) The salt gradient allows water to be withdrawn from the urine (allows the urine to be concentrated). **Explanatory detail**: Because the salt gradient increases through the medulla, the osmotic gradient is maintained and water can be continually withdrawn from the urine.

(b) Salt gradient is produced by the active and passive movement of salt from the filtrate into the extracellular fluid in the medulla.

---

18. Control of Urine Output (page 29)
1. (a) ADH secretion increases: urine volume decreases, blood volume increases.
   (b) ADH secretion decreases: urine volume increases, blood volume decreases.

2. Diabetes insipidus symptoms include the excretion of large amounts of very dilute urine (accompanied by a great thirst).

3. Alcohol inhibits ADH release causing greater urine output, resulting in dehydration and thirst.

4. (a) Aldosterone increases the reabsorption of sodium from the kidney tubules.
   (b) Water follows sodium reabsorption, increasing blood volume.

5. Decreases or increases in blood volume are detected by hypothalamic osmoreceptors and the secretion of ADH increases or decreases accordingly. This results in an adjustment of urine output until homeostasis is restored. The adjustments made in response to the ADH release act back on the hypothalamus to counter further change. Note that, by a more complex mechanism, low blood volumes also stimulate the release of aldosterone, which induces Na^+ reabsorption in the kidney and (by osmosis) more absorption of water and thus restoration of blood volume.

---

19. Kidney Transplants (page 30)
1. Acute renal failure (ARF) arises suddenly as a result of infection, blood loss, or dehydration. ARF is characterised by a very sudden drop in urine volume. Chronic renal failure (CRF) develops over months or years as a result of poorly controlled diabetes or high blood pressure, or chronic kidney disease. Unlike ARF, recovery from CRF is not possible.

2. Creatinine is produced at a relatively constant rate and is usually filtered out by the kidneys, so if the levels increase in the blood it would indicate that the kidneys are not operating normally.

3. Kidney transplantation (if the tissue is a good match) offers a high chance of success and a normal life away from the constraints of continual dialysis. Problems include the need to take immunosuppressant drugs and the risk that a suitable donor will not be available when required. Life-time dialysis is expensive, time consuming and cannot help regulate blood pressure in the way that a kidney can. There is also a risk of infection (this is higher with peritoneal dialysis).

20. Renal Dialysis (page 31)
1. The dialysing solution is constantly being replaced because it needs to be free of urea and other wastes in order to maintain the concentration gradient between the blood and the dialysate. Without a gradient, urea and other wastes would stay in the blood.

2. Other ions and small molecules do not diffuse into the dialysate because they are at a similar concentration in both blood and dialysate, i.e. the dialysate has a similar ionic composition to blood and there is no concentration gradient for these molecules.

3. The urea passes into the dialysate because there is always less urea present in dialysate than in blood. Therefore there is a concentration gradient for urea between the blood and the dialysate.

4. The general transport process involved in dialysis is diffusion; the movement of molecules from a region of high concentration to a region of low concentration.

5. The dialysing solution runs in the opposite direction to that of the blood (similar to countercurrent heat exchangers and countercurrent flow in fish gills) because in this way almost all of the urea can be removed from the blood in the shortest possible time. **Explanatory detail**: The blood at the beginning of the dialysis column (high urea) encounters dialysate that already contains some urea, but there is still a concentration gradient from blood to dialysate. By the time the blood reaches the end of the dialysis column most of the urea has been removed, but it encounters fresh dialysing solution (no urea) and there is still a concentration gradient. Having blood and dialysate running in opposite direction maintains the concentration gradient for a longer time. If the two fluids ran in the same direction the concentrations would quickly equilibrate, and urea would cease to pass into the dialysate.

---

21. Urine Analysis (page 32)
1. Urinalysis is quick and simple to perform and there are diagnostic parameters for particular metabolites. This makes diagnosis and treatment potentially quick and cost-effective.

2. (a) Diabetes
   (b) The presence of red blood cells in the urine (hematouria) and therefore bleeding in the urinogenital tract.

3. Athletes withhold drug use for a period before testing so that the body has had time to break down and metabolise the drug and excrete it (thereby avoiding detection).

---

22. Urine Analysis for Pregnancy Testing (page 33)
1. (a) The reaction zone contains soluble mouse monoclonal anti-HCG AB enzyme conjugates which bind to the HCG hormone.
   (b) The test zone contains polyclonal anti-HCG antibodies, which also bind HCG, and a dye. The enzyme catalyses a reaction with the dye causing a colour change.
   (c) In the control zone, unbound antibody enzyme conjugates bind with the anti-mouse antibodies. The enzyme catalyses a second colour change reaction to confirm the test is working.

2. Only one band would be present (the one showing the test has run correctly).

---

23. Chapter Review (page 34)
No model answer. Summary is the student's own.

---

24. Key Terms: Did You Get It? (page 35)
1. ADH (D), excretion (E), kidney (F), liver (C), loop of Henle (B), nephron (A)

2. (a) The kidney
   (b) The nephron
   (c) Loop of Henle
   (d) ADH and aldosterone

3.

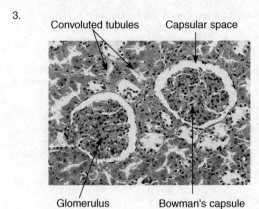

Convoluted tubules   Capsular space

Glomerulus   Bowman's capsule

4.

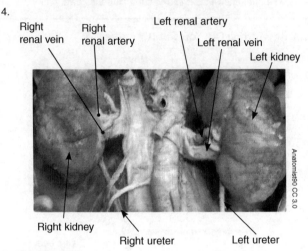

Right renal vein   Right renal artery   Left renal artery

Left renal vein

Left kidney

Anatomist90 CC 3.0

Right kidney

Right ureter   Left ureter

5. (a) The lobule
   (b) Any three of:
   Secretes bile, metabolises amino acids, fats, and carbohydrates, synthesises glucose from non-carbohydrate sources, stroes iron, copper, and vitamins, synthesises cholesterol, converts unwanted amino acids to urea, manufactures, heparin and plasma proteins, detoxifies poisons.
   (c) The bile duct, a branch of the hepatic portal vein, a branch of the hepatic artery.

6. (a) Hepatic portal vein
   (b) Hepatic artery

---

25. Detecting Changing States (page 37)

1. A stimulus is any physical or chemical change in the environment capable of provoking a response in an organism. Organisms may perceive this as a change in pressure, sound or light.

2. (a) Any from the examples provided (or others). Answers provided as stimulus (receptor): Blood pH/carbon dioxide level (chemoreceptors in blood vessels); blood pressure (baroreceptors); stretch (proprioreceptors, e.g. muscle spindle).
   (b) Chemoreceptors maintain breathing and heart rates, baroreceptors maintain blood pressure, proprioreceptors maintain movement, photoreceptors maintain vision.

---

26. The Basis of Sensory Perception (page 38)

1. Sensory receptors convert stimulus energy (e.g. electromagnetic radiation) into electrochemical energy (a change in membrane potential).

2. All receptors receive and respond to stimuli by producing receptor potentials.

3. The stimulus energy opens an ion channel in the membrane leading to ion flux and a localised change in membrane potential, e.g. an influx of Na^+ and a depolarisation. This localised change in membrane potential is called a receptor

potential and it may lead directly or indirectly to an action potential.

4. Receptor potentials are localised depolarisations. They are graded (of different sub-threshold magnitude) and not self-propagating.

---

27. Neurone Structure (page 39)

1. (a) Any one of:
   • Motor neurones have many short dendrites and a single (usually long) axon.
   • In sensory neurones, the cell body gives rise to two axonal branches (one central, one peripheral). The axons are usually short.
   • A sensory neurone has a sense organ at the 'receptor' end or it synapses with a sense organ (as in the retina of the eye). In a motor neurone the dendrites receive their stimuli from other neurones.
   (b) Any one of:
   • Motor neurone transmits impulses from CNS to muscles or glands (effectors).
   • Sensory neurone transmits impulses from sensory receptors to the CNS.

2. (a) Any one of:
   • Motor neurones have a long axon.
   • Relay neurones have a short axon within the CNS.
   (b) Any one of:
   • Motor neurone transmits impulses from CNS to muscles or glands (effectors).
   • Relay neurone transmits impulses from sensory neurones to motor neurones within the CNS.

3. Relay neurones lie within the CNS, so impulses are not transmitted far. The axons of motor neurones extend to effectors in the peripheral NS so their axons are often very long (extending to the periphery of the body).

4. Muscles and glands.

5. (a) Myelination increases the speed of impulse conduction.
   (b) Oligodendrocytes
   (c) Schwann cells
   (d) Neurones in the PNS frequently have to transmit over long distances so speed of impulse conduction is critical to efficient function.

6. (a) Myelination prevents ions from entering or leaving the axon and so stops leakage of charge across the neurone membrane. The current is carried in the cytoplasm so that the action potential at one node (gap in the sheath) is sufficient to trigger an action potential at the next. Myelin also reduces energy expenditure since fewer ions overall need to be pumped to restore resting potential after an action potential has passed.
   (b) Faster conduction speeds enable more rapid responses to stimuli.

7. The destruction of the myelin prevents those (previously myelinated) axons from conducting. Without insulation, the neurone membrane leaks ions and the local current is attenuated and insufficient to depolarise the next node. **Explanatory note**: myelinated axons have gated channels only at their nodes, so action potentials can only be generated at node regions in those axons that were myelinated.

---

28. The Nerve Impulse (page 41)

1. An action potential is a self-regenerating depolarisation (electrochemical signal) that allows excitable cells (such as muscle and nerve cells) to carry a signal over a (varying) distance.

2. (a) Neurones are able to transmit electrical impulses.
   (b) Supporting cells are not able to transmit impulses.

3. (a) Depolarisation: Na^+ channels open and Na^+ ions flood into the cell.
   (b) Repolarisation: Na^+ channels close, K^+ channels open and K^+ ions move out of the cell.

4. (1) When the neurone receives the threshold-level stimulus, the membrane briefly becomes more permeable to Na^+, which

floods into the cell (through voltage gated channels), resulting in a depolarisation. (2) After the Na$^+$ influx, the Na$^+$ gates close and K$^+$ gates open, causing a brief hyperpolarisation before the resting potential is restored.
(3) The hyperpolarisation means that for a short time (1-2 ms) the neurone cannot respond, so the impulse only travels in one direction (away from the stimulus).

5. Resting potential is restored when all voltage activated gates close and the Na$^+$/K$^+$ pump restores the initial balance of ions, moving 2 K$^+$ into the neurone for every 3 Na$^+$ moved out.

6. (a) Action potential travels by saltatory conduction, with depolarisation and action potential generation at the nodes of Ranvier.
   (b) Action potential spreads by local current (conduction is slower).

7. Because the refractory period makes the neurone unable to respond for a brief period after an action potential has passed, the impulse can pass in only one direction along the nerve (away from the cell body).

29. Encoding Information (page 43)
1. (a) Stimulus strength is encoded by the frequency of action potentials.
   (b) Frequency modulation is the only way to convey information about the stimulus strength to the brain because action potentials are 'all or none' (information can not be communicated by variations in amplitude).

2. In the Pacinian corpuscle, stronger pressure produces larger receptor potentials, threshold is reached more rapidly, and action potential frequency is higher.

3. Sensory adaptation allows the nervous system to cease responding to constant stimuli that do not change in intensity. Constant, background sensory information can be ignored.

30. The Cholinergic Synapse (page 44)
1. A **synapse** is a junction between two neurones or between a neurone and an effector (e.g. gland or muscle cell).

2. Arrival of a nerve impulse at the end of the axon causes an influx of calcium. This induces the vesicles to release their neurotransmitter into the cleft.

3. Delay at the synapse is caused by the time it takes for the neurotransmitter to diffuse across the gap (synaptic cleft) between neurones.

4. (a) Neurotransmitter (NT) is degraded into component molecules by enzyme activity on the membrane of the receiving neurone.
   (b) The neurotransmitter must be deactivated so that it does not continue to stimulate the receiving neurone (continued stimulation would lead to depletion of neurotransmitter and fatigue of the nerve). Deactivation allows recovery of the neurone so that it can respond to further impulses.
   (c) Transmission is unidirectional because the synapse is asymmetric in structure and function. The presynaptic membrane does not possess the receptors for the NT and the postsynaptic neurone does not have the stores of NT within vesicles.

5. **The amount of neurotransmitter released** influences the response of the receiving cell (response strength is proportional to amount of neurotransmitter released).

31. Integration at Synapses (page 45)
1. Integration refers to the interpretation and coordination (by the central nervous system) of inputs from many sources (inputs may be inhibitory or excitatory).

2. (a) **Summation**: The additive effect of presynaptic inputs (impulses) in the postsynaptic cell (neurone or muscle fibre).
   (b) **Spatial summation** refers to the summation of impulses from **separate** axon terminals arriving simultaneously at the postsynaptic cell. **Temporal summation** refers to the

arrival of several impulses from a **single** axon terminal in rapid succession (the postsynaptic potentials are so close together in time that they can sum to generate an action potential).

3. (a) **Acetylcholine** is the NT involved. Arrival of an action potential at the neuromuscular junction causes the release of Ach from the synaptic knobs.
   (b) Ach causes **depolarisation** of the postsynaptic membrane (in this case, the sarcolemma). **Explanatory note**: The depolarisation in response to the arrival of an action potential at the postsynaptic cell is essentially the same as that occurring at any excitatory synapse involving Ach neurotransmitter.

32. Chapter Review (page 46)
No model answer. Summary is the student's own.

33. Key Terms: Did You Get It? (page 47)
1.

Across	Down:
4. Potential	1. Depolarisation
6. Dendrite	2. Synapse
8. Receptor	3. Cholinergic
9. Axon	5. Myelin
10. Neurone	7. Effectors
11. Nervous system	

2. (a)

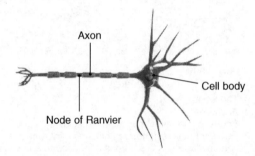

Axon

Cell body

Node of Ranvier

   (b) Myelinated
   (c) Schwann cells can be seen wrapped around the axon. Nodes of Ranvier can also be seen.
   (d) As action potentials (self-propagating depolarisations)

3. (a) Letters should appear in the boxes in this order (top to bottom): B, D, E, C, A
   (b) -70 mV
   (c) Above 50 mV

34. The Basis of Hormonal Control (page 49)
1. (a) Antagonistic hormones: Two hormones that have contrasting (counteracting) effects on metabolism. Examples: insulin and glucagon, parathormone (increases blood calcium) and calcitonin (lowers blood calcium).
   (b) In general principle, the product of a series of (hormone controlled) reactions controls its own production by turning off the pathway when it reaches a certain level. If there is too little of the product, its production is switched on again.

2. Only the target cells have the appropriate receptors on the membrane to respond to the hormone. Other (non-target) cells will not be affected.

3. (a) Hormones must circulate in the blood to reach the target cells and a metabolic response must be initiated. This takes some time.
   (b) Hormones bring about a metabolic change and often start a sequence of cascading, interdependent events, which take some time to conclude. Nervous responses continue only for the time that the stimulation continues.

© 2015 **BIOZONE** International
ISBN: 978-1-927309-16-2
Photocopying Prohibited

35. The Adrenal Glands (page 50)

1. a) The adrenal gland has two functionally and structurally distinct regions, an outer cortex and an inner medulla.
   (b) The medulla secretes adrenaline and noradrenaline into the blood in response to direct sympathetic nervous system stimulation. The adrenal cortex secretes steroid hormones (corticosteroids and androgens). Its secretion is regulated by neuroendocrine hormones secreted from the pituitary gland and by the renin-angiotensin system.

2. Neural (the medulla) and hormonal (adrenal cortex)

3. (a) Adrenaline or noradrenaline: released during stress as part of the fight or flight response.
   (b) Cortisol: stimulates the production of glucose in the liver. Aldosterone: involved in regulating blood pressure and volume through regulation of sodium.

36. Pancreatic Histology (page 51)

1. (a) The islets of Langerhans
   (b) The pancreatic islets produce insulin (from β cells) and glucagon (from α cells) to regulate blood glucose levels. Pancreatic endocrine tissue also has a role in appetite stimulation, neurotransmission, and cell proliferation.

2. Exocrine tissue can be distinguished by the presence of intralobular ducts surrounded by cells making up the pancreatic acini. Endocrine tissue does not have these ducts.

3. Student's own drawing. A sector of tissue is shown below:

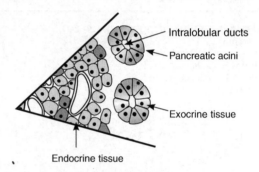

Intralobular ducts

Pancreatic acini

Exocrine tissue

Endocrine tissue

37. Control of Blood Glucose (page 52)

1. (a) Stimulus: Rise in the levels of glucose in the blood above a set level (about 5.6 mmol per L or 100 mg dL^{-1}).
   (b) Stimulus: Fall in blood glucose levels below a set level (about 3.9 mmol per L or 70 mg dL^{-1}).
   (c) Glucagon brings about the production (and subsequent release) of glucose from the liver by the breakdown of glycogen and the synthesis of glucose from amino acids.
   (d) Insulin increases glucose uptake by cells and brings about production of glycogen and fat from glucose in the liver.

2. Fluctuations in blood glucose (BG) and blood insulin levels are closely aligned. Following a meal, BG rises sharply and there is a corresponding increase in blood insulin, which promotes cellular glucose uptake and a subsequent fall in BG. This pattern is repeated after each meal, with the evening meal followed by a gradual decline in BG and insulin over the sleep (fasting) period. Negative feedback mechanisms prevent excessive fluctuations in blood glucose (BG) throughout the 24 hour period.

3. Humoral (blood glucose level).

38. Mechanism of Insulin Secretion (page 53)

1. (a) Glucose transporter protein transports the glucose molecules into the beta cell.
   (b) Rise in intracellular ATP causes ATP-sensitive potassium channels to close.
   (c) Membrane depolarisation activates the voltage-gated Ca^{2+} channels.
   (d) Activation of the voltage-gated Ca^{2+} channels results in Ca^{2+} being transported into the beta cell. This initiates transport of insulin across the membrane into the blood.

2. An extensive network of blood vessels is required to deliver glucose efficiently to the beta cells as the trigger for insulin secretion and to transport secreted insulin from the pancreas and into the general circulation.

3. A two phase release means that the body can quickly respond to a sudden influx of glucose from a meal with very rapid cellular uptake of glucose and then follow this with a more sustained, slower release based on the rate at which the insulin is synthesised, processed and secreted. This keeps blood glucose levels more stable during the 1-2 hours immediately following a meal.

39. Carbohydrate Metabolism in the Liver (page 54)

1. In any order:
   (a) Glycogenesis: the production of glycogen from glucose in the liver, stimulated by insulin.
   (b) Glycogenolysis: breakdown of glycogen to produce glucose, stimulated by adrenaline and glucagon.
   (c) Gluconeogenesis: the production of glucose from non-carbohydrate sources, stimulated by adrenaline and glucocorticoid hormones.

2. (a) Process at 1: Glycogenesis (formation of glycogen from glucose).
   (b) Process at 2: Glycogenolysis (glycogen breakdown).
   (c) Process at 3: Gluconeogensis (formation of glucose from non-carbohydrate sources).

3. Interconversion of carbohydrates is essential to regulating blood glucose levels and maintaining a readily available supply of glucose as fuel without incurring the homeostatic problems of high circulating levels of glucose.

40. Type 1 Diabetes Mellitus (page 55)

1. Hyperglycemia (high blood glucose) results from the inability of cells to take up glucose. Glucose is normally reabsorbed in the kidney tubule, but when blood glucose is too high, the it exceeds the kidney's ability to reabsorb it from the filtrate and so glucose is excreted in the urine (glucosuria). Excessive thirst results from the high urine volumes associated with the excretion of excess glucose. Hunger, fatigue and weight loss result from the inability to utilise glucose. Ketosis results from the metabolism of fats (used because glucose is not entering the cell so cannot be used as an energy source).

2. Regular injections of insulin restore the levels of insulin in the blood, allowing the cells to take up glucose.

41. Type 2 Diabetes Mellitus (page 56)

1. The pancreas still produces insulin but the body's cells do not react to it.

2. Type 1 diabetes results from a non-production of insulin and must be treated with insulin injection. Type 2 results from the body's cells becoming insensitive to normal levels of insulin. It is treated first with dietary management and exercise. Insulin therapy is usually not involved except in severe cases.

42 Treating Diabetes With Stem Cells (page 57)

1. Type 1 diabetes has a single specific cause making it easier to produce a solution, in this case production of β cells. Also there is a lack of donors for pancreatic transplants. Production and implantation of new β cells derived from stem cells can potentially provide a cure for type 1 diabetics.

2. Pluripotent stem cells come from the blastocyst. Induced pluripotent stem cells are differentiated cells (e.g. skin cells) that have been reprogrammed to turn them back into pluripotent cells.

3. (a) The first investigation managed to produce β cells in sufficient numbers for viable transplantation.
   (b) The cells can't be transplanted directly into the patient as they would be destroyed by the patient's immune system.

4. (a) The β cells were able to be produced from skin cells, thus not needing blastocyst cells. Also they are the patient's own cells and therefore won't be rejected by the patient's immune system.

(b) Potentially, the cells would be susceptible to the auroimmune destruction that destroyed the patient's original β cells.

43. Chapter Review (page 58)
No model answer. Summary is the student's own.

44. KEY TERMS: Did You Get it? (page 59)
1

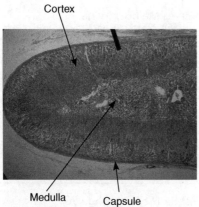

```
P I P D I A B E T E S M E L L I T U S Z R C N G M
D G O P E N D O C R I N E G L A N D T T S V Q D L
G T C P B T N K B B K O A U C E Q K C Q J U P W E
O J V I M P E G Z M J L V M E D U L L A F D V N E
A J I S L E T S O F L A N G E R H A N S W V I J J
Z P Y H R M U N M H O Q V B S Y Z P J I O L O P D
G Q K O O F K V V N V F X V U B E H A N A O L Q K
F C G R L U O N T R S J Q D T P X X L N A P C U W
E B A M T J L R C J L V J T H W P Q E M C R K U A
Q E X O C R I N E G L A N D A W L R Z B E R P R I
E U N N B C K W O S D P S G S V D B C I L P E V
O I O E I N S U L I N Z B Q Y A C T J N T H O A V
X H L S W Q H S J A Y A D R E N A L G L A N D S S
Z B L N O T G L U C A G O N U M H S V P U N Q A G
```

(a) Hormones
(b) Endocrine gland
(c) Insulin
(d) Pancreas
(e) Adrenaline
(f) Glucagon
(g) Islets of Langerhans
(h) Exocrine gland
(i) Diabetes mellitus
(j) Adrenal glands
(k) Medulla

2.

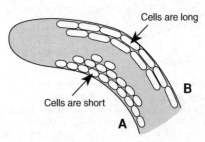

Cortex

Medulla   Capsule

3. (a) Regulate blood glucose levels.
   (b) Negative feedback
   (c) The pancreas

4. (a) Glycogenesis is the production of glycogen from glucose. Glycogenolysis is the breakdown of glycogen to glucose.
   (b) The liver.

45. Plant Responses to Abiotic Stress and Herbivory (page 61)
1. (a) Plants must be able to adapt to changes in the physical environment as they are not able to move when the changes occur.
   (b) Examples include: opening and closing of stomata in response to water loss. Opening and closing of flowers in response to temperature.

2. Chemical means of protection include producing tannins and alkaloids which affect the taste of the leaf or may be toxic. Plants may use chemical signals to enlist the help of animals for protection (e.g. ants).

   Physical means of protection include thorns, spines, and silica in the leaves.

46. Nastic Responses (page 62)
1. Nastic responses are independent of stimulus direction and are often quite rapid (compared with growth responses).

2. (a) Thermonasty   (b) Photonasty

3. Disturbance causes a change in membrane potential to the cells at base of each leaflet. The cells lose tugor, causing them to collapse.

47. Tropisms and Growth Responses (page 63)
1. (a) Positive chemotropism
   (b) Negative geotropism
   (c) Positive hydrotropism
   (d) Positive phototropism
   (e) Positive geotropism
   (f) Positive thigmomorphogenesis (*alt.* thigmotropism)

2. (a) Enables roots to turn and grow down into the soil (where they obtain moisture and nutrients).
   (b) Enables coleoptiles to turn up and grow towards the sunlight (necessary for food manufacture).
   (c) Enables the plant to clamber upwards and grow toward the light instead of possibly becoming smothered by more upright plants.
   (d) Enables pollen tube to locate the micropyle of the embryo sac, and sperm nuclei to fertilise the egg.

3. Tropisms show adaptive value because they help position a plant to achieve the most favourable conditions. For example, positive phototropism orientates seedlings to grow towards the sunlight, and helps them obtain enough light for photosynthesis.

48. Investigating Phototropism (page 64)
1. (a) Auxin.
   (b) Positive phototropism.
   (c) **Point A**: Cells stay short.
       Point B: Cells elongate.
   (d) Side B
   (e)

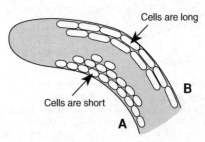

Cells are long

Cells are short

B

A

2. The hormone is produced in the shoot tip. The light initiates the response.

3. **Plant A**: The plant will exhibit phototropism and bend towards the sun.
   Plant B: The plant will exhibit no phototropic behaviour and will not bend.

49. Investigating Geotropism (page 65)
1. (a) In shoots, more auxin accumulates on the lower side of the shoot. In response to higher auxin levels here, the cells on the lower side of the stem elongate and the shoot tip turns up.
   (b) In roots, the accumulation of auxin on the lower side inhibits elongation (since this is the response of roots to high auxin). The cells on the upper side therefore elongate more than those on the lower side and the root tip turns down.

2. (a) Approx. 10–3 mg L^{-1} (b)   Stem growth is promoted.

3. (a) A negative geotropic response ensures shoots turn up towards the light (important when light may be absent as when buried deeply in soil).
   (b) Positive geotropism ensures roots turn down into the soil so that they can begin obtaining the water and minerals required for continued growth.

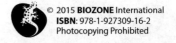

50. Investigation of Geotropism in Roots (page 66)
1. (a) Down (towards the ground).
   (b) The root began to curve towards the ground.
   (c) The direction of the pull of gravity relative to the root had changed and so the root curved to compensate for the change of direction and continue to grow down.
   (d)

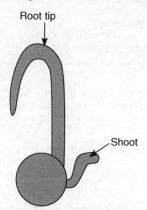

Root tip

Shoot

2. (a) Up (away from the ground)
   (b) The shoot continued to grow away from the ground.
   (c) The shoot reorientated itself to grow away from the ground, as this is the direction in which it is most likely to find light.

51. Regulating Seasonal and Daily Events (page 67)
1. Gibberellic acid (GA) increased the height of the seedlings for the first four months of the experiment, with the mean height of seedlings treated with GA being greater than for the control (no GA). Increase in seedling height corresponded to GA concentration, with the greatest mean seedling height occurring at the highest GA concentration. After five months there was little to no difference between the height of seedlings with and without GA.

2. As the leaf ages, auxin levels drop making it more sensitive to ethylene. Ethylene is involved in the production of enzymes (e.g. cellulase) that break down the cell wall at the bases of the petiole, causing the leaf to fall.

3. ABA regulates stomatal closure. During drought, ABA levels increase, causing K^+ and Cl^- (and then water by osmosis) to leave the guard cell, closing the stomata.

52. Transport and Effects of Auxin (page 68)
1. Positive phototropism

2. In an experiment in which a cut stem with an auxin-infused agar block is uppermost and an agar block without auxin is at the base, auxin moves down the stem. However, if the system is inverted, no auxin is found in the stem, indicating that the auxin in the agar was not transported or diffused through the stem - it only travels one way.

3. Auxin causes cell elongation.

53. The Role of Auxins in the Apical Dominance (page 69)
1. Auxins in the growing leaves of the apical bud are synthesised in concentrations high enough to suppress the growth of the buds below. Consequently, the main shoot grows more vigorously than the lateral shoots.

2. Auxin is produced in the growth regions of young plants (e.g. apical tip). If the apical tip of a young seedling remains intact, no lateral growth occurs. If the apical tip is removed, there is lateral growth. Conclusion: the presence of auxin in the apical tip of young seedlings inhibits lateral growth.

3. (a) and (b)

Apical bud

Lateral bud

(c) The apical buds.
(d) Their production of auxin inhibits the lateral buds so that the plant keeps growing upwards (towards light).

4. By nipping off the apical buds and encouraging lateral growth.

54. How Gibberellins Affect Growth (page 70)
1. and 2.

Table 1 Height of control / cm

	2	4	6	9	11	18	20
Mean	1.2	3.3	4.7	6.6	8.5	13.2	15.8
SD	0.5	0.3	0.4	0.4	0.8	2.0	2.6

Table 2 Height gibberellin treatment / cm

	2	4	6	9	11	18	20
Mean	0.8	5.8	14.0	23.4	26.6	33.5	35.2
SD	0.3	0.7	1.0	1.2	0.9	3.3	4.2

3. (a)

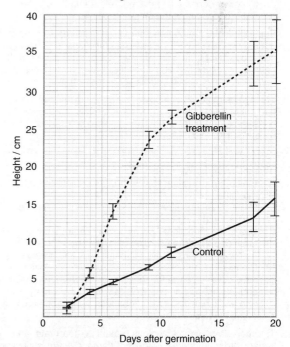

Effect of gibberellin on plant growth

(b) Gibberellin increases the height of the plant.
(c) Yes
(d) The difference is significant as the error bars do not overlap between treatment and control.
(e) A Student's t - test could be used as there are two

populations being investigated (control and gibberellin).
(f) $t = 8.78$. Degrees of freedom = 8. The difference is significant to $p = 0.001$

5. The peas do not produce gibberellins so when gibberellin is added the effect can be attributed to the treatment.

6. The peas with gibberellin will grow tall and the group with gibberellin and the inhibitor will show a result similar to the control because the gibberellin and gibberellin inhibitor will counteract each other to produce no additional growth effect.

55. Commercial Use of Plant Hormones (page 72)

1. Plant hormones can be used by growers in several ways. Cytokinins can be sprayed on fruit to inhibit fruit fall, giving fruit more time to ripen. Gibberellins can be used to increase fruit size in apples and improve fruit set. Auxins also improve fruit set. Auxins and gibberellins can also be applied to unpollinated flowers to encourage the growth of seedless fruit. Alternatively fruit can be picked early and shipped to market. Ethylene is then used to ripen the fruit before it is sold. Gibberellins and auxins are also used to promote growth of seedlings and plants so that they reach harvestable size more quickly. ABA can be used to promote seed dormancy while gibberellin is used to promote germination in plants requiring a cold period to germinate. PlaA monosynaptic reflex involves only one synapse (two neurons), whereas a polysynaptic reflexxnt hormones are also used in selective weed killlers.

56. The Mammalian Nervous System (page 73)

1. The three main functions of the nervous system is to detect stimuli, interpret them, and coordinate a response.

2. (a) **CNS**: Brain and spinal cord (nervous tissue extending down back and protected by the spinal column).
    (b) The brain has ultimate control of almost all body activities (except simple spinal reflexes). The spinal cord interprets simple reflexes and relays impulses to and from the brain.

3. (a) **PNS**: All nerves and sensory receptors outside the CNS. Divided into sensory and motor divisions. The motor division controls both voluntary (somatic) and involuntary (autonomic) responses.
    (b) Receives sensory information, relays impulses to the CNS, brings about the motor response.

4. Separation of the motor division of the PNS into somatic and autonomic divisions allows essential functions to occur without conscious involvement. In this way, the conscious part of the brain is not overwhelmed by having to coordinate every motor response. This improves efficiency of motor function.

5. The sympathetic NS is active when the body is preparing for fight or flight. The parasympathetic NS is more active in conserving energy and replenishing energy reserves ('feed or breed' or 'rest and digest').

57. The Human Brain (page 75)

1. **A:** Cerebrum. Function: Higher thought processes (conscious thought).
    B: Cerebellum. Function: Coordinates body movements, posture and balance.
    C: Brainstem. Function: Acts as a relay centre between the brain and the spinal cord. Also is involved autonomic functions such as breathing, heart rate, and swallowing.
    D: Diencephalon (thalamus and hypothalamus). Thalamus acts as relay centre for sensory messages. Hypothalamus controls the autonomic nervous system and links nervous and endocrine systems. It regulates sleep, appetite, thirst and body temperature.

2. The medulla oblongata controls breathing, heart rate, and various other autonomic reflexes. If damage death is likely as these functions will be impaired.

3. The primary somatic sensory area receives information from the skin, muscles, and viscera. It allows recognition of pain, temperature, and touch.

4. The primary motor area controls muscle movement. Each side controls the activity on the opposite side of the body.

5. (a) Breathing/heartbeat: brainstem (medulla)
    (b) Memory/emotion: cerebrum
    (c) Posture/balance: cerebellum
    (d) Autonomic functions: hypothalamus
    (e) Visual processing: occipital lobe
    (f) Body temperature: hypothalamus
    (g) Language: motor and sensory speech areas
    (h) Muscular movement: primary motor area

58. Reflexes (page 77)

1. Higher reasoning is not a preferable feature of reflexes because it would slow down the response time. The adaptive value of reflexes is in allowing a very rapid response to a stimulus.

2. A spinal reflex involves integration within the spinal cord, e.g. knee jerk (monosynaptic) or pain withdrawal (polysynaptic). A cranial reflex involves integration within the brain stem (e.g. pupil reflex).

3. (a) The knee jerk reflex helps to maintain posture and balance when walking. Being a reflex it requires no conscious though and means the brain is not devoting energy to correcting posture while walking.
    (b) The blink reflex protects the eye against damage by foreign bodies.
    (c) The grasp reflex in infants ensures the infant remains attached to its mother (e.g. grasping fur in primates or a hand in humans).
    (d) The pupillary light reflex regulates light entering the retina and ensures bright light does not damage the retina.

59. Coordination by Nerves and Hormones (page 78)

1.

	Nervous control	Hormonal
Communication		Hormones in blood
Speed	Very rapid	Relatively slow
Duration	Short term	Longer lasting
Target pathway	Through nerves to specific cells	
Action	Causes glands to secrete or muscles to contract	Causes changes in metabolic activity.

60. Flight or Fight (page 79)

1. (a) Stimulus originating from the hypothalamus causes the adrenal glands to release catecholamines, e.g. adrenaline, which prepare the body for action (fight or flight) by increasing heart rate and blood pressure, and mobilising glucose. Blood flow to the brain and muscles is increased and metabolic rate increases.
    (b) After the stress is relieved, impulses from the hypothalamus are reduced, sympathetic output falls, catecholamine secretion declines, and heart rate and blood pressure return to normal.

2. Adrenaline acts as a first messenger to the cell, binding to cell membrane receptors and leading to activation of the enzyme adenylate cyclase. Andenylate cyclase activates the second messenger cAMP, which triggers a cascade of phosphorylation reactions in the cell that eventually leads to the (amplified) cellular response.

61. Nerves and Hormones Regulate Heart Rate (page 80)

1. (a) **Increased venous return**: Heart rate increases.
    (b) **Release of adrenaline**: Heart rate increases.
    (c) **Increase in blood CO_2**: Heart rate increases.

2. These effects are mediated through the cardiovascular center

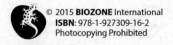

(sympathetic output via the cardiac nerve).

3. Physical exercise increases venous return (blood returning at a faster rate to the heart).

4. (a) Cardiac nerve.
   (b) Vagus nerve.

5. Increased stretch in the vena cava indicates increased venous return and cardiac output must increase to cope with the increase. Increased stretch in the aorta indicates increased cardiac output and heart rate decreases. The two responses keep cardiac output regulated according to the body's needs.

62. Physiological Response to Exercise (page 81)

Popn A $\bar{x}_A = 88.48$ $n_A = 21$ $s_A = 13.17$

Popn B $\bar{x}_B = 136.48$ $n_B = 21$ $s_B = 34.17$

Null hypothesis: There is no difference between mean heart rate before and after exercise.

x length / mm		x − x̄ (deviation from the mean)		(x − x̄)² (deviation from mean)²	
Pre exercise (A)	Post exercise (B)	Pre exercise	Post exercise	Pre exercise	Post exercise
72	87	-16.5	-49.5	272.25	2450.25
116	175	27.5	38.5	756.25	1482.25
79	96	-9.5	89.9	-40.5	1638.6
97	100	8.5	72.6	-36.5	1330.8
90	176	1.5	2.3	39.5	1561.8
67	132	-21.5	461.4	-4.5	20.1
115	176	26.5	703.3	39.5	1561.8
82	141	-6.5	42.0	4.5	20.4
95	113	6.5	42.5	-23.5	551.3
82	136	-6.5	42.0	-0.5	0.2
77	96	-11.5	131.8	-40.5	1638.6
105	153	16.5	272.9	16.5	272.9
79	90	-9.5	89.9	-46.5	2160.4
99	152	10.5	110.7	15.5	240.9
82	156	-6.5	42.0	19.5	381.0
87	170	-1.5	2.2	33.5	1123.6
82	128	-6.5	42.0	-8.5	71.9
98	172	9.5	90.6	35.5	1261.7
80	132	-8.5	71.9	-4.5	20.1
95	141	6.5	42.5	4.5	20.4
79	144	-9.5	89.9	7.5	56.6
$n_A = 21$	$n_B = 21$			$\Sigma(x - \bar{x})^2$ 3471.2	$\Sigma(x - \bar{x})^2$ 17865.2

1. Variance PopA = 173.56
   Variance PopB = 893.26

2. -48

3. Variance A÷nA = 8.26
   Variance B ÷nB = 42.54
   Sum of (A÷nA) + (B ÷nB) = 50.80
   $\sqrt{50.8} = 7.13$
   $t$calc = -6.73 (take absolute value)

4. d.f = 21 + 21 = 42 - 2 = 40

5. 2.021

6. (a) Reject null hypothesis
   (b) The calculated t value at 0.05 is much higher than the critical t value. Thus the null hypothesis of no difference

can be rejected.

7. (a) Population B (post exercise)
   (b) People do not respond uniformly to exercise as some may be more or less conditioned than others. A greater range of heart rates post exercise could therefore be expected.

8. Exercise has a significant effect on heart rate.

63. Types of Muscle (page 83)

1. **Smooth muscle**, also called involuntary muscle, has spindle shaped cells with one central nucleus per cell and a smooth appearance with no striations. Its contractions are diffuse and it is not under conscious control so it is involved in movement of visceral organs such as the gut.
   Striated (skeletal) muscle is voluntary and is responsible for the skeletal muscle movement over which we have conscious control. It has a striated or striped appearance. The cells are multinucleate with peripheral nuclei.
   Cardiac muscle is involuntary muscle responsible for the contraction of the heart muscle. Although it is striated, it does not fatigue in the same way as skeletal muscle (it has a built in refractory or rest period). There is one nucleus per cell and electrical junctions called intercalated discs join individual cells (rapid transmission of action potentials).

2. Skeletal muscle is under conscious control. Cardiac and smooth muscle are involuntary and not under conscious control.

64. Muscles and Movement (page 84)

1. Muscles can only contract and relax, therefore they can only pull on a bone; they cannot push it. To produce movement, two muscles must act as **antagonistic** pairs to move a bone to and from different positions. Note that other synergistic muscle sometimes assist the action of the prime movers.

2. The freedom of movement in a joint depends directly on the type of joint. Some joints allow movement in every plane (e.g. ball and socket joints), while others only allow movement in one plane (e.g. hinge joints).

65. Skeletal Muscle Structure and Function (page 85)

1. (a) The banding pattern results from the overlap pattern of the thick and thin filaments (dark = thick and thin filaments overlapping, light = no overlap).
   (b) **I band**: Becomes narrower as more filaments overlap and the area of non-overlap decreases.
   H zone: Disappears as the overlap becomes maximal (no region of only thick filaments).
   Sarcomere: Shortens progressively as the overlap becomes maximal.

2. (a) Relaxed
   (b) The I band can clearly be seen. If the muscle was contracted the I band would not be present.

3. Fast twitch fibres. Fast twitch fibres have rapid contraction rates, rapid rates of ATP production, and high power generation. They work anaerobically, but fatigue quickly, and these properties suit them to short bursts of activity where maximal force is required quickly (as in sprinting).

66. Neuromuscular Junction (page 87)

1. (a) The neuromuscular junction is a specialised cholinergic synapse formed where a motor neurone terminates on the sarcolemma (plasma membrane) of a muscle fibre. It consists of the axon terminal (synaptic end bulb) and the region of the sarcolemma it makes contact with.
   (b) Acetylcholine
   (c) An action potential is stimulated in the sarcolemma. The action potential is propagated through the muscle fibre, causing the release of Ca^{2+} from the sarcoplasmic reticulum (and contraction of the muscle fibre).

2. (a) The muscle fibres contract fully or not at all.
   (b) Varying amounts of force can be produced by contracting recruiting more muscle fibres to be active. A large force requires a large number of muscle fibres.

67. The Sliding Filament Theory (page 88)

1. (a) Myosin: Has a moveable head that provides a power stroke when activated.
   (b) Actin: Two protein molecules twisted in a double helix shape that form the thin filament of a myofibril.
   (c) Calcium ions: Bind to the blocking molecules, causing them to move and expose the myosin binding site.
   (d) Troponin-tropomyosin: Bind to actin molecule in a way that prevents myosin head from forming a cross bridge.
   (e) ATP: Supplies energy for flexing of the myosin head (power stroke).

2. (a) ATP (hydrolysis) and Ca^{2+} (to expose the binding sites).
   (b) Ca^{2+} is released from the sarcoplasmic reticulum. ATP is produced by cellular respiration in the mitochondria.

3. Muscle fibres use a lot of ATP during contraction. Having many mitochondria ensures a good ATP supply.

68. Energy for Muscle Contraction (page 89)

1. The glycolytic system won't supply enough ATP for prolonged activity. Continued anaerobic metabolism results in a build up of hydrogen ions which ultimately impedes contraction.

2. **Energy systems**:
   ATP-CP
   ATP supplied by: Breakdown of CP
   Duration of ATP supply: Short (3-15 s)
   Glycolytic
   ATP supplied by: Anaerobic breakdown of glycogen
   Duration of ATP supply: A few minutes at most.
   Oxidative
   ATP supplied by: Complete aerobic (oxidative) breakdown of glycogen to CO_2 and water.
   Duration of ATP supply: Prolonged but dependent on ability to supply oxygen to the muscles (fitness).

3. (a) Region **A**: Oxygen deficit: the amount of oxygen needed for aerobic supply but not supplied by breathing, i.e. an oxygen deficit builds up.
   (b) Region **B**: Oxygen debt: the extra oxygen required (taken in) despite the drop in energy demand. The debt is used to replace oxygen reserves, restore CP, and break down lactic acid.
   Note: Both components (deficit and debt) are often used synonymously (as oxygen debt) although they are not quite the same. The deficit is the oxygen shortfall incurred during exercise; the debt is the amount of oxygen required to restore oxygen and energy stores to resting levels. Their values are not necessarily the same.

4. Oxygen uptake does not immediately return to resting levels because of the extra oxygen required to restore oxygen and energy levels (the oxygen debt).

5. Oxygen supply is increased by increased rate and depth of breathing (increasing gas exchange rate) and increased blood flow (increased gas transport).

6. Lactic acid levels in the blood rise for a time after exercise because excess lactic acid is transported in the blood from the muscles (where it has accumulated) to the liver, where it is metabolised to CO_2 and water.

69. Muscle Fatigue (page 91)

1. Muscle performance declines because of a fall in ATP generation and available calcium. These changes are the result of a fall in pH and elevated levels of phosphate.

2. In a long distance race, such as a marathon, ATP continues to be produced **aerobically** until all energy supplies are exhausted. In a sprint, ATP is produced **anaerobically** until accumulation of H+ impairs muscle contraction.

70. Measuring Muscle Fatigue (page 92)

1 (a) Graph based on student results. Generally the line should trend down over time.
   (b) Student results. Generally the number of times the peg is opened will decline over time.

(c) Student answer as per results.
(d) In most cases the number of peg openings will be lower.

71. Chapter Review (page 93)

No model answer. Summary is the student's own.

72. KEY TERMS: Did You Get It? (page 94)

1. (a) Phototropism
   (b) Geotropism (or gravitropism)
   (c) Nasty or nastic response
   (d) Auxin

2. (a) Positive phototropism by the shoot, negative phototropism by the roots.
   (b) Light

3. actin (I), auxin (R), cardiac muscle (O), central nervous system (A), cerebellum (P), cerebrum (N), cyclic AMP (L), gibberellin (E), muscle fatigue (F), muscle fibre (D), myosin (Q), neuromuscular junction (J), peripheral nervous system (K), reflex (C), second messenger (B), skeletal muscle (M), sliding filament hypothesis (G), smooth muscle (H)

73. Energy in Cells (page 96)

1. (a) Photosynthesis: Carbon dioxide and water.
   (b) Cellular respiration: Oxygen and glucose.

2. Glucose (or pyruvate).

3. Solar energy (the Sun).

4. Food (plants and other animals).

74. Photosynthesis (page 97)

1. (a) Grana: Stacks of thylakoid membranes containing chlorophyll molecules. They are the site of the light dependent reactions of photosynthesis, which involve light energy capture via photosystems I and II.
   (b) Stroma: The liquid interior of the chloroplast in which the light independent phase takes place. This biochemical process involves carbon fixation (production of carbohydrate) via the Calvin cycle.

2. (a) Carbon dioxide: Comes from the air (through stomata) and provides carbon and oxygen as raw materials for the production of glucose. Some oxygen molecules contribute to the production of H_2O.
   (b) Oxygen: Comes from CO_2 gas (through stomata) and H_2O (via the roots and vascular system). The oxygen from the CO_2 is incorporated into glucose and H_2O. The oxygen from water is given off as free oxygen (a waste product).
   (c) Hydrogen: Comes from water (via the roots and vascular system) from the soil. This hydrogen is incorporated into glucose and H_2O. **Note**: To clarify: isotope studies show that the carbon and oxygen in the carbohydrate comes from CO_2, while the free oxygen comes from H_2O.

3. Triose phosphate is converted to glucose, which is fuel for respiration and used to construct disaccharides (e.g. sucrose), cellulose, or starch. Oxygen is used for aerobic respiration and water is recycled and even reused for photosynthesis.

75. Chloroplasts (page 98)

1. (a) Stroma   (d) Granum
   (b) Stroma lamellae   (e) Thylakoid
   (c) Outer membrane   (f) Inner membrane

2. (a) Chlorophyll is found in the thylakoid membranes.
   (b) Chlorophyll is a membrane-bound pigment found in and around the photosystems embedded in the membranes. Light capture by chlorophyll is linked to electron transport in the light dependent reactions.

3. The internal membranes provide a large surface area for binding chlorophyll molecules and capturing light. Membranes are stacked in such a way that they do not shade each other.

4. Chlorophyll absorbs blue and red light but reflects green light, so leaves look green to the human eye.

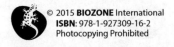
© 2015 **BIOZONE** International
ISBN: 978-1-927309-16-2
Photocopying Prohibited

76. Pigments and Light Absorption (page 99)

1. The **absorption spectrum** of a pigment is that wavelength of the light spectrum absorbed by a pigment, e.g. chlorophyll absorbs red and blue light and appears green. Represented graphically, the absorption spectrum shows the relative amounts of light absorbed at different wavelengths.

2. Accessory pigments absorb light wavelengths that chlorophyll *a* cannot absorb, and they pass their energy on to chlorophyll *a*. This broadens the action spectrum over which chlorophyll *a* can fuel photosynthesis.

77. Separation of Pigments by Chromatography (page 100)

1. (a) and (b)

   A: Rf value 0.92. Pigment: carotene
   B: Rf value 0.53. Pigment: Chlorophyll a
   C: Rf value: 0.46. Pigment: Chorophyll b
   *Note: exact replication of the Rf values may not always occur. In this example, Chlorophyll a and b can be recognised due to their relative positions and closeness to the correct Rf values.
   D: Rf value: 0.30. Pigment: Xanthophyll

2. There should be no effect on the Rf values but the amount of separation will be reduced.

78. Light Dependent Reactions (page 101)

1. NADP: Carries protons (H^+) from the light dependent phase to the light independent reactions.

2. Chlorophyll molecules trap light energy and produce high energy electrons. These are used to make ATP and NADPH. The chlorophyll molecules also split water, releasing H^+ for use in the light independent reactions and liberating free O_2.

3. Light dependent (D) phase takes place in the grana (thylakoid membranes) of the chloroplast and requires light energy to proceed. The light dependent phase generates ATP and reducing power in the form of NADPH. The electrons and hydrogen ions come from the splitting of water.

4. The ATP synthesis is coupled to electron transport. When the light strikes the chlorophyll molecules, high energy electrons are released by the chlorophyll molecules. The energy lost when the electrons are passed through a series of electron carriers is used to generate ATP from ADP and phosphate.

   Note: ATP is generated (in photosynthesis and cellular respiration) by chemiosmosis. As the electron carriers pick up the electrons, protons (H^+) pass into the space inside the thylakoid, creating a high concentration of protons there. The protons return across the thylakoid membrane down a concentration gradient via the enzyme complex, ATP synthase, which synthesises ATP.

5. (a) Non-cyclic phosphorylation: Generation of ATP using light energy during photosynthesis. The electrons lost during this process are replaced by the splitting of water.
   (b) The term non-cyclic photophosphorylation is also (commonly) used because it indicates that the energy for the phosphorylation is coming from light.

6. (a) In cyclic photophosphorylation, the electrons lost from photosystem II are replaced by those from photosystem I rather than from the splitting of water. ATP is generated in this process, but not NADPH. Note: In the cell, both cyclic and non-cyclic photophosphorylation operate to different degrees to balance production of NADPH and ATP.
   (b) The non-cyclic path produces ATP and NADH in roughly equal quantities but the Calvin cycle uses more ATP than NADPH. The cyclic pathway of electron flow makes up the difference.

7.

	Non-cyclic phosphorylation	Cyclic phosphorylation
Photosystem	I and II	I
Energy carrier produced	NADPH, ATP	ATP
Photolysis of water	Yes	No
Production of oxygen	Yes	No

79. Light Independent Reactions (page 103)

1. (a) 6   (d) 12   (g) 2
   (b) 6   (e) 12   (h) 1
   (c) 12 (f) 6

2. RuBisCo catalyses the reaction that splits CO_2 and joins it with ribulose 1,5-bisphosphate. It fixes carbon from the atmosphere.

3. Triose phosphate (note that you may also see this referred to as glyceraldehyde-3-phosphate, GALP, G3P or PGAL)

4. $6CO_2 + 18ATP + 12\ NADPH\ + 12H^+$
   $\rightarrow 1$ glucose $+18ADP + 18Pi +12\ NADP^+ + 6H_2O$

5. The Calvin cycle will cease in the dark in most plants because the light dependent reactions stop, therefore no NADPH or ATP is produced. At night, stomata also close, reducing levels of CO_2 (there will still be some CO_2 in the leaf as a waste product of respiration).

80. Experimental Investigation of Photosynthesis (page 104)

1. $DCPIP + 2H^+ + 2e^- \rightarrow DCPIPH_2$

2. Hill's experiment showed that water must be the source of the oxygen liberated in photosynthesis.

3. The reactions happen very quickly. By taking the sample only seconds apart, each step of the reaction can be worked out by recording the order of appearance of the reaction products.

81. The Fate of Glucose (page 105)

1. Glucose has three main fates: storage, building macromolecules, or production of usable energy (ATP).

2. In plants, glucose can be converted to (any one of): fructan (energy storage in vacuoles), starch (energy storage in plastids), or cellulose (cell wall component).

3. Glucose is produced using a ^{13}C or ^{14}C. When the glucose is used to make other molecules, the carbon isotopes can be detected by the radioactivity or the change in density of tissues or products in which the carbon has been incorporated.

82. Factors Affecting Photosynthesis (page 106)

1. (a) CO_2 concentration: Photosynthetic rate increases as the CO_2 concentration increases, and then levels off.
   (b) Light intensity: Photosynthetic rate increases rapidly as the light intensity increases and then levels off.
   (c) Temperature: Increased temperature increases the photosynthetic rate, but this effect is not marked at low concentrations of CO_2.

2. The photosynthetic rate is determined by the rate at which CO_2 enters the leaf. When this declines because of low atmospheric levels, so does photosynthetic rate.

3. (a) By changing only one factor at a time (temperature or CO_2 level) it is possible to assess the effects of each one.
   (b) CO_2 has the greatest effect of these two variables.
   (c) At low levels of CO_2, increase in temperature has little effect (the rate of CO_2 entry into the leaf is the greatest determinant of photosynthetic rate).

4. Glasshouses are controlled environments in which the levels of light, humidity, temperature, and CO_2 can be optimised to maximise photosynthetic rate. In particular, CO_2 enrichment in an environment where transpiration losses are minimised enables maximum productivity.

5. Student's own experimental design. Possible hypothesis is that temperature will increase the rate of photosynthesis within limits (H_0 being no effect of temperature). The choice of design and plant will be up to the student but an easy one to choose is to measure the rate of oxygen (air bubble) production in a submerged aquatic macrophyte such as *Elodea*. The temperature can then be easily changed by heating or cooling the water. Things the student should make reference to and explain if necessary:

   – the control and how it was set up
   – how the dependent variable (biological response) is to be measured and how many measurements will be made
   – how the independent variable (temperature) is to be varied and the range of that variation
   – how other variables are kept constant and the value of these variables (e.g. light level)
   – how many plants at each treatment level

83. Investigating Photosynthetic Rate (page 107)
1. Missing figures for bubbles per minute are (in order of low light intensity to high light intensity): 0, 2, 3, 4, 6, 11, 11.67

2.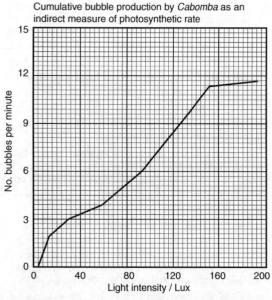

3. Photosynthetic rate increases with increasing light intensity. Although light intensity theoretically drops off at a constant rate, this may not practically occur due to shadows, variations in the equipment being used, or other light pollution. It is therefore better to measure the light intensity rather than infer light intensity from distance.

4. The gas was oxygen.

5. Instead of counting the bubbles (which could vary in volume) the gas could be collected and the volume produced measured. This could be done by displacement of water in a graduated cylinder or by using a photosynthometer.

84. Chapter Review (page 108)
No model answer. Summary is the student's own.

85. KEY TERMS: Did You Get It? (page 109)
1. (a) Water (or carbon dioxide)
   (b) Carbon dioxide (or water)
   (c) Photosynthesis
   (d) Oxygen

(e) Glucose
2. (a) Water + carbon dioxide → glucose + oxygen
   $H_2O + CO_2 \rightarrow C_6H_{12}O_6 + O_2$
   (b) Photosynthesis takes place in the chloroplasts.

3. absorption spectrum (G), accessory pigments (H), action spectrum (I), Calvin cycle (D), chlorophyll (J), grana (K), light dependent phase (F), photosynthesis (A), ribulose bisphosphate (B), stroma (E), thylakoid discs (C)

4.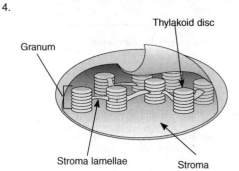

86. The Role of ATP in Cells (page 111)
1. Organisms need to respire so that the energy in food can be converted, via a series of reactions, into the energy yielding molecule, ATP, which powers metabolic reactions.

2. (a) Mitochondria are the site for the Krebs cycle and ETS stages of cell respiration and ATP production.
   (b) The mitochondrion is separated into regions (compartmentalised) by membranes. This allows certain metabolic reactions, together with their required enzymes, to be isolated in a specific region. All of the required components are in one place, increasing efficiency.

3. Maintaining body temperature (thermoregulation) is requires energy input. ATP is required for the muscular activity involved in shivering (used to heat the body). ATP is also required for the secretion of sweat (used to cool the body).

87. ATP and Energy (page 112)
1. (a) The hydrolysis of ATP is coupled to the formation of a reactive intermediate, which can do work. Effectively, the hydrolysis of ATP to ADP + Pi releases energy.
   (b) Like a rechargeable battery, the ADP/ATP system alternates between high energy and low energy states. The addition of a phosphate to ADP recharges the molecule so that it can be used for cellular work.

2. Glucose

3. The folded inner membrane of a mitochondrion greatly increases the surface area. This allows more ATP synthase molecules to be accommodated on the membrane and therefore increases the ability to produce ATP.

4. Highly active cells require a lot of energy (ATP) to move. Therefore, they have large numbers of mitochondria so that enough ATP can be produced to meet their energy demands.

88. ATP Production in Cells (page 113)
1. (a) Glycolysis: cytoplasm
   (b) Link reaction: matrix of mitochondria
   (c) Krebs cycle: matrix of mitochondria
   (d) Electron transport chain: cristae (inner membrane surface) of mitochondria.

2. The ATP generated in glycolysis and the Krebs cycle is generated by substrate level phosphorylation, i.e. transfer of a phosphate group directly from a substrate to ADP. In contrast, the ATP generated via the electron transport chain is through oxidative phosphorylation, a step-wise series of redox reactions that provide the energy for forming ATP. Oxidative phosphorylation yields much more ATP per glucose than substrate level phosphorylation.

 © 2015 **BIOZONE** International
ISBN: 978-1-927309-16-2
Photocopying Prohibited

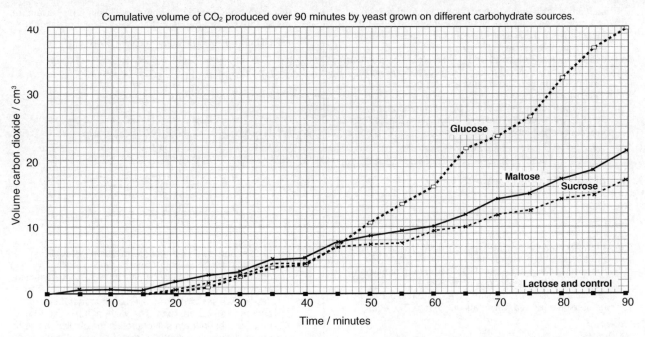

Cumulative volume of CO_2 produced over 90 minutes by yeast grown on different carbohydrate sources.

89. The Biochemistry of Respiration (page 114)

1.

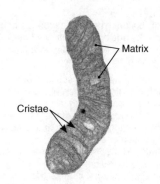

2. The link reaction prepares pyruvate for entry in the Krebs cycle. Carbon dioxide is removed and coenzyme A is added.

3. (a) 6   (b) 3   (c) 2   (d) 6   (e) 5   (f)4

4. (a) Glycolysis: 2 ATPs
   (b) Krebs cycle: 2 ATPs
   (c) Electron transport chain: 34 ATPs
   (d) Total produced: 38 ATPs

5. The carbon atoms lost are lost as CO_2 molecules.

6. During oxidative phosphorylation, ADP is phosphorylated to ATP. Electrons passed along the electron transport chain are used to pump hydrogen ions across the inner membrane of the mitochondria. The flow of hydrogen ions back across the membrane is coupled to the phosphorylation of ADP to ATP. Oxygen is the final electron acceptor, reducing hydrogen to water. Because oxygen is the final acceptor the process is called oxidative phosphorylation.

90. Chemiosmosis (page 116)

1. In chemiosmosis, ATP synthesis is coupled to electron transport and movement of hydrogen ions. Energy from the passage of electrons along the chain of electron carriers is used to pump protons (H^+), against their concentration gradient, into the intermembrane space, creating a high concentration of protons there. The protons return across the membrane down a concentration gradient via the enzyme complex, ATP synthase, which synthesises the ATP.

2. Elevating the H^+ concentration outside the exposed inner mitochondrial membranes would cause them to move down their concentration gradient via ATP synthase, generating ATP.

3. A suspension of isolated chloroplasts would become alkaline because protons would be removed from the medium as ATP was generated.

4. (a) By placing chloroplasts in an acid medium, the thylakoid interior was acidified. Transfer to an alkaline medium established a proton gradient from the thylakoid interior to the medium.
   (b) The protons could flow down the concentration gradient established, via ATP synthase, and generate ATP.

91. Anaerobic Pathways (page 117)

1. **Aerobic respiration** requires the presence of oxygen and produces a lot of useable energy (ATP). **Fermentation** does not require oxygen and uses an alternative H^+ acceptor. There is little useable energy produced (the only ATP generated is via glycolysis).

2. (a) $2 \div 38 \times 100 = 5.3\%$ efficiency
   (b) Only a small amount of the energy of a glucose molecule is released in anaerobic respiration. The remainder stays locked up in the molecule.

3. The build up of ethanol, which is toxic to cells, inhibits further metabolic activity.

92. Investigating Yeast Fermentation (page 118)

1. $C_6H_{12}O_6 \rightarrow C_2H_5OH + 2CO_2$

2. Calculated rate of CO_2 production, group 1:
   (a) None: $0 \ cm^3min^{-1}$ or $0 \ cm^3s^{-1}$
   (b) Glucose: $0.443 \ cm^3min^{-1}$ or $7.4 \times 10^{-3} \ cm^3s^{-1}$
   (c) Maltose: $0.24 \ cm^3min^{-1}$ or $4.0 \times 10^{-3} \ cm^3s^{-1}$
   (d) Sucrose: $0.191 \ cm^3min^{-1}$ or $3.2 \times 10^{-3} \ cm^3s^{-1}$
   (e) Lactose: $0 \ cm^3min^{-1}$ or $0 \ cm^3s^{-1}$

3. The assumptions made are that 24°C and pH 4.5 provide suitable (even optimal) conditions for yeast fermentation. This is reasonable as it has been stated in the background that the literature cites warm, slightly acidic conditions as optimal for baker's yeast.

4. Graph of results: see above.

5. (a) Time
   (b) 0 - 95 minutes in 5 minute increments.
   (c) Minutes

6. (a) Volume of CO_2 produced
   (b) cm^3

7 (a) The fermentation rates were greatest for the substrate glucose, with a CO_2 yield approximately twice that for maltose and sucrose. Maltose and sucrose were similar to

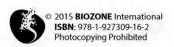

each other, while there was no fermentation of lactose.

(b) CO_2 production is highest when glucose is the substrate because it is directly available as a fuel and requires no initial hydrolysis to use.

(c) Maltose (glucose-glucose) and sucrose (glucose-fructose) must first be hydrolysed before the glucose is available (the fructose from sucrose must also be isomerised to glucose).

(d) Lactose cannot be metabolised by yeast, presumably because yeast lack the enzyme to hydrolyse the galactose and glucose that form this disaccharide.

8. CO_2 production would increase more rapidly.

93. Respiratory Quotient (page 120)
1. (a) 0.71
    (b) Fat

2. (a) 1
    (b) 0.70
    (c) After 48 hours the available carbohydrate has been used and stored fat is being respired.
    (d) There is no difference in the RQ. The amount of oxygen required and CO_2 released during respiration of any particular substrate is constant. The difference is how fast the substrate is used, which affects O_2 and CO_2 equally.

3. A: Fat
    B: Protein
    C: Carbohydrate

94. Measuring Respiration (page 121)
1. Oxygen is being used so the air pressure in the chamber is dropping, moving the bubble towards the chamber.

2. (a) Missing values (in order from 10 minutes to 25 minutes):
    8, 6, 7, 6
    (b)

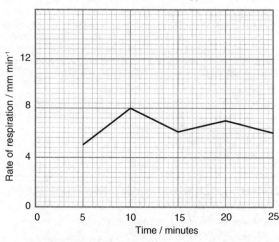

Rate of respiration in maggots

(c) After an initial small peak at 10 minutes, the rate of respiration is relatively constant.
(d) The animals might take time to adjust to the new conditions so a wait period before recording allows for this.

3. Changes to atmospheric pressure or temperature which might affect the movement of the bubble affect both sides equally so cancel each other out and only the oxygen used would be measured.

95. Chapter Review (page 122)
No model answer. Summary is the student's own.

96. KEY TERMS: Did You Get It? (page 123)
1. aerobic respiration (H), alcoholic fermentation (E), anaerobic respiration (P), ATP (Q), cellular respiration (K), chemiosmosis (B), electron transport chain (N), glycolysis (A), Krebs cycle (J), lactic acid fermentation (G), link reaction (D), matrix (M),

mitochondria (C), oxidative phosphorylation (O), pyruvate (L), respiratory substrate (I), substrate level phosphorylation (F)

2. (a) RQ of two seedlings during early germination:

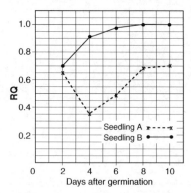

(b) Both seedlings began their germination metabolising primarily fats for energy. However, while seedling A continued to metabolise mainly fats (with some synthesis of carbohydrate and organic acids), throughout the 10 day period, seedling B rapidly moved to metabolising carbohydrate alone. **Note**: The value of 0.91 (seedling B) may have been the result of protein metabolism alone or (more likely) respiration of a mix of fat and glucose.

97. Gene Mutations (page 125)
1. A **frame shift mutation** occurs when the sequence of bases is offset by one position (by adding or deleting a base). This alters the order in which the bases are grouped as triplets and can severely alter the amino acid sequence.

2. (a) Reading frame shifts and nonsense substitutions.
    (b) They may cause large scale disruption of the coded instructions for making a protein. Either a completely wrong amino acid sequence for part of the protein or a protein that is partly completed (missing amino acids due to an out-of-place terminator codon).
    (c) A substitution mutation to the third base in a codon. Because of degeneracy in the genetic code, a substitution at the third base position may not change the amino acid that is encoded.

3. (a) Silent mutation.
    (b) The mutation is less likely to affect the individual because the same amino acid is coded for, and therefore the same protein will be produced. Note that current research indicates that even silent mutation can exert some effect on the way DNA is handled in the cell.
    (c) Evolutionary biologists can use these mutations to create a molecular clock (base change per unit time) which they can use to determine the degree of relatedness between species (time since divergence).

98. The Nature of Mutation (page 126)
1. Mutagens increase the mutation rate of DNA, producing errors in the DNA sequence. Mutagens include UV light, tobacco smoke, and some types of chemicals and viruses. Damage to the DNA causes incorrect proteins to be produced or may damage genes that regulate cell division, resulting in cancer.

2. Somatic mutations occur in the body (somatic) cells and are not inherited. They may affect an individual within its lifetime. Gametic mutations may be inherited and can therefore affect descendents.

3. The mutation does not extend to the seeds (the gametic portion that will be inherited).

4. A beneficial mutation confers a selective advantage in terms of fitness whereas a harmful mutation has a deleterious effect on fitness. Effects apply in the prevailing environment.

5. (a) A silent mutation changes the codon (usually the third base), but does not change the amino acid encoded by the DNA sequence.

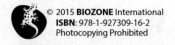

(b) A change in the exonic sequence can disrupt RNA splicing sites or make the mRNA unstable, leading to translation errors.

99. A Beneficial Mutation (page 128)
1. (a) High levels of cholesterol in the blood is a risk factor for the development of cardiovascular disease.
   (b) ApoA1 is a component of HDL which transport cholesterol to the liver, clearing it from bloodstream.
   (c) The amino acid arginine is replaced by cysteine.

2. ApoA1 Milan is more efficient at transporting excess cholesterol to the liver, clearing it from the blood faster so that it cannot damage the cardiovascular system.

3. The gene was not diluted by a large population. Marriages between related people may have helped to maintain the gene within the population.

100. Gene Mutations and Genetic Diseases (page 129)
1. (a) Gene name: HBB   Chromosome: 11
   Mutation type: Substitution.
   (b) Gene name: CFTR   Chromosome: 7
   Mutation type: autosomal recessive. Great range: deletion, missense, nonsense, misplaced terminator codon. Most common is a deletion of 3 nucleotides.
   (c) Gene name: HTT (aka IT15)   Chromosome: 4
   Mutation type: autosomal dominant. Duplication (CAG repeats of varying length).

2. The disease does not become apparent until mid-adulthood by which time a sufferer has likely already had children.

3. CF reduces susceptibility to cholera, a fatal disease. Cholera pandemics have killed millions in the recent past and cholera is endemic (persistent at a low level) in many populations. Sickle cell anaemia persists because heterozygotes have considerable resistance to malaria, a disease still common in tropical parts of the world.

101. Sickle Cell Mutation (page 130)
1. (a) Bases: 21   (b) Triplets: 7   (c) Amino acids: 7

2. (a) A point mutation, a base substitution, causes one amino acid to change in the β- chain of the haemoglobin molecule.
   (b) The mutated haemoglobin protein behaves differently to the normal haemoglobin, so that when not carrying oxygen, it precipitates out into fibres which deform the RBC to a sickle cell shape.
   (c) Heterozygotes (carriers) of the sickle cell mutation have both normal and mutated haemoglobin molecules. The have enough functional haemoglobin to carry sufficient oxygen, so only suffer minor effects of the disease.
   (d) The mutated haemoglobin is less soluble at low oxygen tensions. In low oxygen environments (such as at altitude) the mutated haemoglobin will precipitate out and the carrier will show symptoms of sickle cell disease.

3. The sickle cell mutation affords some degree of resistance to malaria and so persists where malaria is present.

102. Cystic Fibrosis Mutation (page 131)
Diagram error: DNA strand should be labelled template strand as in the question (not coding strand). Apologies for any confusion. This error has subsequently been fixed.

1. (a) mRNA: GGC ACC AUU AAA GAA AAU AUC AUC UUU GGU GGU
   (b) Mutant mRNA: GGC ACC AUU AAA GAA AAU AUC AUC | GGU GGU
   (c) A deletion mutation.

2. (a) The abnormal CFTR protein is rapidly degraded in the cell and so does not insert into the plasma membrane.
   (b) Water moves into the cells because of the accumulation of chloride ions.

103. Gene Induction in Prokaryotes (page 132)
1. (a) Operon: Consists of at least one structural gene coding for the primary enzyme structure, and two regulatory elements: the operator and the promoter.
   (b) Regulator gene: (repressor gene) produces a repressor substance that binds to the operator, preventing transcription of the structural genes.
   (c) Operator: This is a non-coding sequence of DNA that is the binding site for the repressor molecule.
   (d) Promoter: Site of RNA polymerase binding to start the transcription process.
   (e) Structural genes: Genes responsible for producing enzymes that control the metabolic pathway.

2. (a) In an inducible enzyme system, the enzymes required for the metabolism of a particular substrate are produced only when the substrate is present. This saves the cell energy in not producing enzymes that have no immediate use.
   (b) Inducible enzyme systems are not adaptive when the substrate is present all (or most) of the time.
   (c) Regulation of a non-inducible system is achieved (in prokaryotes) through gene repression, Genes that are normally switched on are switched off.

3. The operon model explains diauxic growth because when the preferred substrate (glucose) is available, the operon is switched off. When only lactose is available, the operon is switched on and lactose is utilised. The lag in the graph is the time taken to switch on the genes and synthesise the enzymes (proteins) needed to metabolise lactose.

104. Gene Control in Eukaryotes (page 134)
1. (a) Promoter: A DNA sequence where RNA polymerase binds and starts transcription.
   (b) Transcription factors: These are proteins that recognise and bind to the promoter sequence and to the enhancer sequence and thereby facilitate initiation of transcription.
   (c) Enhancer sequence: The DNA sequence to which the transcription factors called activators bind. This binding is important in bringing the activators in contact with the transcription factors bound to the RNA polymerase at the promoter.
   (d) RNA polymerase: The enzyme that, with the initial aid of transcription factors, transcribes the gene.
   (e) Terminator sequence: Nucleotide sequences at the end of a gene that function to stop transcription.

2. Difference between gene control in prokaryotes and eukaryotes (any one of):
   - Eukaryotic genes are not found as operons; the control sequences may be some distance from the gene to be transcribed.
   - In eukaryotic gene expression, the transcription factors are important; only when the transcription factors are assembled can the gene be transcribed.
   - Eukaryotic gene expression involves the formation of hairpin loop in the DNA which brings the transcription factors and polymerase into contact.

105. Post Transcriptional Modification (page 135)
1. Primary mRNA can be spliced and combined in many different ways. This allows more proteins to be produced than the number of genes in the human genome. Post translational modification also allows for more protein variations to be produced.

2. There are four main ways in which mRNA can be modified to code for different proteins. (1) Exon skipping can leave out one or more parts of the mRNA. (2) Intron retention retains parts of the primary mRNA that would normally be left out. (3) Mutually exclusive exons can produce two alternative proteins, and (4) some exons have more than one binding site, which produces exons of different lengths and different proteins.

3. Being able to modify the mRNA allows an organism to produce alternative proteins without needing an entirely new gene to code for it. This ensures that the organism's genome is not too large. Note: For example, the Dscam gene in *D. melanogaster* can produce more than 38 000 proteins from the one gene.

106. Protein Activation by Cyclic AMP (page 136)

1. (a) Adrenaline acts as the first messenger (binds to receptor on the outside of the cell).
   (b) cAMP acts as the second messenger. It activates protein kinase, beginning a phosphorylation cascade that amplifies the signal.

2. (a) Reversible phosphorylation allows the signal to be switched off quickly and for the proteins to be recycled.
   (b) The proteins can be used again. This saves the cell energy and the response time is much faster than if the proteins were degraded and had to be resynthesised.

107. Homebox Genes and Development (page 137)

1. (a) A homeobox gene is a gene containing a conserved DNA sequence of 180 base pairs called the homeobox.
   (b) The homeodomain encodes a string of amino acids, which bind to DNA and act as a transcription factor (regulating the expression of other genes).

2. (a) Hox genes are a special group of homeobox genes that are found only in animals.
   (b) Hox genes control the development of the back and front parts of the animal body.

3. (a) The same genes are present in essentially all taxa, and they have not changed much during their evolutionary history.
   (b) Homeobox sequences must be fundamentally important to the development of the organism. Mutations are likely to have a profound and deleterious effect on morphology or functionality so the sequences tend to remain static (i.e. mutations when they occur are fatal and not passed on).

3. The occurrence of Hox genes in clusters indicates that it is important that the genes are linked and inherited together as a unit; disruption by crossing over and recombination would not be adaptive.

4. Changes in gene expression can bring about changes in morphology, e.g. in differences in neck length in vertebrates. Neck length is controlled by expression of the Hox c6 gene. Where it is expressed marks the boundary between neck and trunk vertebrae, e.g. in snakes, the boundary is shifted forward to the base of the skull with no neck results, while in geese the boundary is shifted backwards and a long neck results.

108. The Timing of Development (page 139)

1. (a) Morphogens act as signal molecules, governing the pattern of tissue development by forming a gradient in the developing tissues.
   (b) Bicoid forms a gradient in the developing Drosophila that signals the development of the anterior regions (high concentration) and posterior regions (low concentration).

2. In sequential induction, a signal molecule induces a response in a cell, which responds by developing and producing another signal molecule and so on in a sequence. C. elegans, sequential induction is seen in the formation of the vulva. The anchor cell signals induce changes in the P6p cell, which in turn induces the development of the P5p and P7p cells.

109. Controlling the Development of Body Form (page 140)

1. Genes are switched on and off in a pattern different to that when the cell is not under stress. This alters the cell cycle, which is not returned to normal until the stress is removed.

2. (a) The M-phase cell contained M-phase promoting factor (MPF). A cell in the G2 phase is preparing to enter M phase. Injecting the cytoplasm of an M-phase cell into a G2-phase cell results in the MPF triggering the change to M phase.
   (b) MPF is made up of two subunits (CDK and cyclin). Cyclin activates CDK, but is not constantly present in the cell. Thus MPF activity is regulated by the presence of cyclin.

3. The rate of apoptosis in the developing limb has been too low to remove the tissue between the digits before the close of the developmental sequence (hence the lack of differentiation between the two toes, which remain partly joined).

4. Apoptosis helps maintain adult cell numbers and is a defence against damaged or infected cells.

5. Any two of the following:
   - Resorption of the larval tail during amphibian metamorphosis.
   - Sloughing of the endometrium during menstruation.
   - The formation of the proper connections (synapses) between neurones in the brain (this requires that surplus cells be eliminated by apoptosis).
   - Controlled removal of virus-infected cells.
   - Controlled removal of cancerous cells.

110. Chapter Review (page 142)

No model answer. Summary is the student's own.

111. KEY TERMS: Did You Get It? (page 143)

1. apoptosis (B), gene expression (A), gene induction (D), homeobox genes (I), Hox genes (C), lac operon (F), morphogens (H), mutation (G), transcription factors (E)

2. (a) An operon consists of a group of closely linked genes, including promoter, where the RNA polymerase binds, an operator, where a repressor molecule can bind, and the structural genes to be transcribed.
   (b) Prokaryotes.

3. (a) Point deletion at the sixth base (G).
   (b) Point insertion at the eleventh base (A).

4. Whether a mutation is harmful or beneficial often depends on the environment (unless the mutation is fundamental to cellular operations). For example, a mutation that causes a light coloured fur coat in a rabbit may be beneficial if the rabbit moves into a lighter environment (e.g. open grassland or snowfields) but it may be harmful in an environment where light colours stand out, e.g. a forest floor.

5. Organisms need to control gene expression to produce and maintain form. During development, genes are switched on or off at specific times, producing signalling molecules such as hormones or proteins, that are required for correct development. Failure to produce these correctly results in an incorrect growth response (e.g. delayed apoptosis during digit formation) which may be harmful to the organism, e.g. limbs that are not formed properly or cancers later in life.

112. Sources of Phenotypic Variation (page 145)

1. (a) During crossing over and independent assortment.
   (b) i: Crossing over allows chromosome to swap genetic information, increasing variation in the gametes.
   ii: Independent assortment randomly assigns chromosomes to gametes, so a large number of chromosome combinations can occur in the gametes.

2. A organism's phenotype can be influenced by the action of the environment on the expression of genes. Environmental factors can include nutrition, availability of light, prevailing wind, temperature, and environmental stress. For example, growth depends on availability of nutrients. A lack of nutrients means the organism may not reach its genetic potential, e.g. a plant with chlorosis has yellowish leaves instead of green due to a lack of magnesium and iron.

113. Describing Alleles (page 146)

1. (a) Heterozygous: Each of the homologous chromosomes contains a different allele for the gene (one dominant and one recessive).
   (b) Homozygous dominant: Each of the homologous chromosomes contains an identical dominant allele.
   (c) Homozygous recessive: Each of the homologous chromosomes contains an identical recessive allele.

2. (a) Aa   (b) AA   (c) aa

3. Each chromosome of a homologous pair comes from a

© 2015 **BIOZONE** International
ISBN: 978-1-927309-16-2
Photocopying Prohibited

different parent: one of maternal origin, one of paternal origin (they originated from the egg and the sperm that formed the zygote). They contain the same sequence of genes for the same traits, but the versions of the genes (alleles) on each chromosome may differ.

4. Alleles are different versions of the same gene. Different alleles provide phenotypic variation for the expression of a gene. There are often two alleles for a gene, one dominant and one recessive. In this case, the dominant allele will be expressed in the phenotype. Sometimes alleles for a gene can be equally dominant, in which case, both alleles will be expressed in the phenotype. Where three or more alleles for a gene exist in a population, there is more phenotypic variation in the population (for that phenotypic character) than would be the case if there were just two alleles.

114. Basic Genetic Crosses (page 147)
1. Punnett square:

	(YR)	(Yr)	(yR)	(yr)
(YR)	YYRR	YYRr	YyRR	YyRr
(Yr)	YYRr	YYrr	YyRr	Yyrr
(yR)	YyRR	YyRr	yyRR	yyRr
(yr)	YyRr	Yyrr	yyRr	yyrr

2. Yellow-round: 9/16   Yellow-wrinkled: 3/16
   Green-round: 3/16   Green-wrinkled: 1/16

3. Ratio: 9 : 3 : 3 : 1

115. Monohybrid Cross (page 148)
1.

	Genotype	Phenotype
Cross 2	50% BB 50% Bb	100% black
Cross 3	25% BB 50% Bb 25% bb	75% black 25% white
Cross 4	100% BB	100% black
Cross 5	50% Bb 50% bb	50% black 50% white
Cross 6	100% bb	100% white

116. Problems Involving Monohybrid Inheritance (page 149)
1. 1/2 Ww and 1/2 ww.

   Ratio: 1 wire-haired : 1 smooth haired

   Working: Parental genotypes are Ww X Ww. The test cross of the F1 (to the homozygous recessive by definition) is to a smooth haired dog (ww).

   1/4 of the F1 will be wire-haired (WW). When crossed with ww the result will be all wire-haired dogs (Ww).

   1/2 the F1 will be wire-haired (Ww). When crossed with ww, the result is 1/2 wire-haired and 1/2 smooth-haired.

   1/4 of the F1 will be smooth-haired (ww). When crossed with ww, all offspring will be smooth-haired (ww). Across all progeny, half will be Ww and half will be ww.

2. Probability of black offspring: (2/3 x 1/4=) 1/6 or 0.16

   Working: The parents genotypes are Bb X Bb, and 1/3 of the white offspring (BB) crossed with Bb will result in no black lambs while 2/3 of the white offspring (Bb) crossed with Bb will result in 1/4 black lambs.

3. (a) They have an albino child (aa) as well as unaffected ones (AA or Aa), so the parents must both be Aa. Note: There is a 25% chance that any child of theirs will be albino.
   (b) The family are all aa.
   (c) The albino father must be aa. The mother must be Aa. The three unaffected children are Aa.
   Note: There is a 50% chance that any child of theirs will be albino. The observed 3:1 ratio is not surprising, given

the small number of offspring.

4. – **Couple #1** genotypes must be $X^H X-$ and $X^H Y$ because neither is affected. Their son is affected $X^h Y$. If the mother is $X^H X^H$ they could not have an affected son. If she is $X^H X^h$, there is a 50% chance that her son will be $X^h Y$.
   – **Couple #2** genotypes must be $X^H X-$ and $X^h Y$ and their son is $X^H Y$. The father did not pass an X chromosome to his son, so his genotype is irrelevant. If the mother is $X^H X^H$, all of her sons will be $X^H Y$, but if she is a carrier $X^H X^h$, there is a 50% chance that her son will be $X^h Y$.
   – Either the hospital or the parents could be correct. The answer depends on the genotype of the mothers.

5. There is a possibility that the male is the father of the child as blood group O can result from crossing AO and BO genotypes. However there are also many other possible outcomes. Without more precise testing or knowing the actual genotypes of the male and female it is impossible to conclusively say the male is the father of the child.

117. Codominance of Alleles (page 150)
1. Two or more alleles are dominant over any recessive alleles and both are fully expressed.

2. (a) Diagram labels:

	White bull	Roan cow
Parent genotype:	$C^W C^W$	$C^R C^W$
Gametes:	C^W, C^W	C^R, C^W
Calf genotypes:	$C^R C^W, C^W C^W$	$C^R C^W, C^W C^W$
Phenotypes:	roan, white	roan, white

   (b) Phenotype ratio: 50% roan, 50% white (1:1)
   (c) By breeding only from the roan calves. Offspring of roan parents should include white, roan, and red phenotypes. By selecting only the red offspring from this generation it would be possible to breed a pure herd of red cattle.

3. (a) Diagram labels:

	Unknown bull	Roan cow
Parent genotype:	$C^R C^R$	$C^R C^W$
Gametes:	C^R, C^R	C^R, C^W
Calf genotypes:	$C^R C^R, C^R C^W$	$C^R C^R, C^R C^W$
Phenotypes:	red, roan	red, roan

   (b) Unknown bull: red bull

4. The phenotypic ratio would be 1 red: 2 roan: 1 white

118. Codominance in Multiple Allele Systems (page 151)
1. Blood group table:
   Blood group **B** BB, BO
   Blood group **AB** AB

2.

Cross 2	**Group O**	**Group O**
Gametes:	O, O	O, O
Children's genotypes:	OO, OO, OO, OO	
Blood groups:	O, O, O, O	

Cross 3	**Group AB**	**Group A**
Gametes:	A, B	A, O
Children's genotypes:	AA, AO, BA, BO	
Blood groups:	A, A, AB, B	

Cross 4	**Group A**	**Group B**
Gametes:	A, A	B, O
Children's genotypes:	AB, AO, AB, AO	
Blood groups:	AB, A, AB, A	

119. Sex Linked Genes (page 152)
1. Parent genotype: $X^O X^O$ $X^O Y$
   Gametes: X^O, X^O X^O, Y
   Kitten genotypes: $X^O X^O, X^O Y, X^O X^O, X^O Y$

	Genotypes	Phenotypes
Male kittens:	$X^O Y$	Black
Female kittens:	$X^O X^O$	Tortoiseshell

2. Parent genotype: $X^O X^O$ $X^O Y$
   Gametes: X^O, X^O X^O, Y
   Kitten genotypes: $X^O X^O, X^O X^O$ $X^O Y, X^O Y$
   Phenotypes: Orange female,   Black male,
                   Tortoise female   Orange male

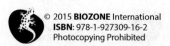

© 2015 **BIOZONE** International
ISBN: 978-1-927309-16-2
Photocopying Prohibited

(a) Father's genotype: X^{O}Y
(b) Father's phenotype: Orange

3. Parent genotype: X^{o}X^o X^{O}Y
    Gametes: X^o, X^o X^O, Y
    Kitten genotypes: X^{O}X^o, X^{o}Y   X^{O}X^o, X^{o}Y
    Phenotypes: Tortoise female,   Tortoise female,
                   Black male   Black male
    (a) Father's genotype: X^{O}Y
    (b) Father's phenotype: Orange
    (c) Yes, the same male cat could have fathered both litters.

4. Parent: Normal wife   Affected husband
    Parent genotype: XX   X^{R}Y
    Gametes: X, X   X^R, Y
    Children's genotypes: X^{R}X, XY   X^{R}X, XY
    Phenotypes: Affected girl,   Affected girl,
                      Normal boy   Normal boy
    (a) Probability of having affected children = 50% or 0.5
    (b) Probability of having an affected girl = 50% or 0.5
        However, all girls born will be affected = 100%
    (c) Probability of having an affected boy = 0% or none

5. Parent: Affected wife   Normal husband
    Parent genotype: X^{R}X   XY
    Gametes: X^R, X   X, Y
    Children's genotype: X^{R}X, X^{R}Y XX, XY
    Phenotypes: Affected girl,   Normal girl,
                      Affected boy   Normal boy

    Note: Because the wife had a normal father, she must be heterozygous since her father was able to donate only an X-chromosome with the normal condition.

    (a) Probability of having affected children = 50% or 0.5
    (b) Probability of having an affected girl = 25% or 0.25
        However, half of all girls born may be affected.
    (c) Probability of having an affected boy = 25% or 0.25
        However, half of all boys born may be affected.

Background for question 6: Sex linkage refers to the location of genes on one or other of the sex chromosomes (usually the X, but a few are carried on the Y). Such genes produce an inheritance pattern which is different from that shown by autosomes:

–   Reciprocal crosses produce different results (unlike autosomal genes that produce the same results).
–   Males carry only one allele of each gene.
–   Dominance operates in females only.
–   A 'cross-cross' inheritance pattern is produced: father to daughter to grandson, etc.

6. **Sex linkage** (in humans, this usually means X-linkage) is involved in a number of genetic disorders. X-linked disorders are commonly seen only in males, because they have only one locus for the gene and must express the trait. If the sex linked trait is due to a recessive allele, females will express the phenotype only when homozygous recessive. It is possible for females to inherit a double dose of the recessive allele (e.g. a colour blind daughter can be born to a colour blind father and mother who is a carrier), but this is much less likely than in males because sex linked traits are relatively uncommon. Over a hundred X-linked genes are known, including those that control:

–   Blood clotting: A recessive allele for this gene causes haemophilia. It affects about 0.01% of males but is almost unheard of in females.
–   Normal colour vision: A recessive allele causes red-green colour blindness affecting 8% of males but only 0.7% of females.
–   Antidiuretic hormone production: A version of this gene causes some forms of diabetes insipidus.
–   Muscle development: A rare recessive allele causes Duchene muscular dystrophy.

120. Inheritance Patterns (page 154)
1. Autosomal recessive:
    (a) Punnett square:
        Male parent phenotype:
        Normal, carrier
        Female parent phenotype:
        Normal, carrier
    (b) Phenotype ratio:
        Normal 3   Albino 1

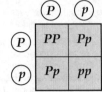

2. Autosomal dominant:
    (a) Punnett square:
        Male parent phenotype:
        Woolly hair
        Female parent phenotype:
        Woolly hair
    (b) Phenotype ratio:
        Normal 1   Woolly 3

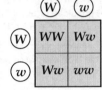

3. Sex linked recessive:
    (a) Punnett square:
        Male parent phenotype:
        Normal
        Female parent phenotype:
        Normal, carrier
    (b) Phenotype ratio:
        Females:
        Normal 2   Haemophiliac 0
        Males:
        Normal 1   Haemophiliac 1

4. Sex linked dominant:
    (a) Punnett square:
        Male parent phenotype:
        Affected (with rickets)
        Female parent phenotype:
        Affected (with rickets)
    (b) Phenotype ratio:
        Females:
        Normal 0   Rickets 2
        Males:
        Normal 1   Rickets 1

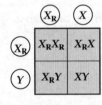

121. Dihybrid Cross (page 155)
1

	BL	Bl	bL	bl
BL	BBLL	BBLl	BbLL	BbLl
Bl	BBLl	BBll	BbLl	Bbll
bL	BbLL	BbLl	bbLL	bbLl
bl	BbLl	Bbll	bbLl	bbll

1 BBLL   2 BbLL   2 BBLl   4 BbLl
1 BBll   2 Bbll
1 bbLL   2 bbLl
1 bbll

122. Inheritance of Linked Genes (page 156)
1. Linkage refers to the situation where genes are located on the same chromosome. As a result, the genes tend to be inherited together as a unit.

2. Gene linkage reduces the amount of variation because the linked genes are inherited together and fewer genetic combinations of their alleles are possible.

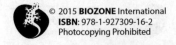
© 2015 **BIOZONE** International
ISBN: 978-1-927309-16-2
Photocopying Prohibited

3.

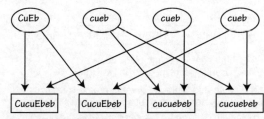

4. (a) CucuEbeb, Cucuebeb, cucuEbeb, cucuebeb
   (b) Offspring genotype: All CucuEbeb (heterozygotes)
   Offpsring phenotype: All wild type (straight wing, grey body)

5. Female gametes = VgEb and vgEb
   Male gametes = vgeb
   Offspring:
   Genotypes: VgvgEbeb   vgvgEbeb
   Phenotypes: straight wing, grey body. Vestigial wing, grey body

6. *Drosophila* produce a wide range of mutations, have a short reproductive cycle, produce large numbers of offspring and are easy to maintain in culture.

123. Recombination and Dihybrid Inheritance
(page 158)
1. It produces new associations of alleles in offspring.

2.

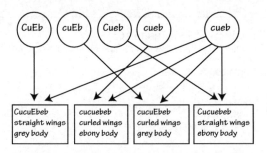

3. Parental linkage groups separate and new associations of alleles are formed in the offspring. The offspring show new combinations of characters that are unlike the parental types.

4. A greater than 50% recombination frequency indicates that there is independent assortment (the genes must be on separate chromosomes).

5. Female gametes: CuY , cuY
   Male gametes: Cuy, cuy
   Offspring genotypes and phenotypes:
   CuCuYy, CucuYy, CucuYy: Straight wings grey body
   cucuYy: Curly wings grey body

124. Detecting Linkage in Dihybrid Crosses (page 160)
1. Expected ratios as follows:
   Purple, long (P_L_)   215
   Purple, round (P_ll)   71
   Red, long (ppL_)   71
   Red, round (ppll)   24
   Total 381

2. (a) Expected ratios all 710 for each genotype as a 1:1:1:1 ratio is expected.
   (b) Parental (given), recombinant, recombinant, parental.
   (c) Morgan performed a test cross.

3. (a) Nail-patella syndrome is dominant. We can tell this because nearly all of the affected individuals had at least one parent with the disease.
   (b) The affected parent was blood group B. All of their offspring with the B blood group also had nail-patella syndrome. Therefore, nail-patella syndrome is linked to the B blood group allele.
   (c) Individual III-3 does not have nail-patella syndrome despite having the B blood type. It is likely that

recombination has occurred, so this individual has not received the nail-patella gene.

126. Chi-Squared Exercise in Genetics (page 162)
1. (a) H0: "If both parents are heterozygous and there is independent assortment of alleles (no linkage) then we would expect to see a 9:3:3:1 ratio of phenotypes in the offspring ".
   (b) HA: "If both parents are heterozygous and the genes are linked (i.e. on the same chromosome), then we would expect the ratios of phenotypes in the offspring to deviate from the 9:3:3:1".

2. (a) Completed table:

Category	O	E	O − E	$(O - E)^2$	$\frac{(O - E)^2}{E}$
Purple stem, jagged leaf	12	16.3	−4.3	18.5	1.1
Purple stem, smooth leaf	9	5.4	3.6	13	2.4
Green stem, jagged leaf	8	5.4	2.6	6.8	1.3
Green stem, smooth leaf	0	1.8	−1.8	3.2	1.8
	Σ 29				Σ 6.6

Expected frequencies calculated as follows:
Purple stem, jagged leaf = 9/16 x 29 = 16.3
Purple stem, smooth leaf = 3/16 x 29 = 5.4
Green stem, jagged leaf = 3/16 x 29 = 5.4
Green stem, smooth leaf = 1/16 x 29 = 1.8
Note: Whole numbers could be used in preference to rounding to one decimal place.
   (b) χ^2 = 6.6
   (c) Degrees of freedom = (4-1=) 3
   (d) The critical value of χ^2 at P = 0.05 and at d.f.= 3 is 7.82. The calculated χ^2 value is less than the critical value (6.6 < 7.82).
   (e) We cannot reject H0: There was no significant difference between the observed results and the expected phenotype ratio of 9:3:3:1. We must conclude that the genes controlling stem colour and leaf shape in tomatoes are on separate chromosomes (unlinked).

3. (a) H0 and HA as for question 1.
   (b) Completed table:

Category	O	E	O − E	$(O - E)^2$	$\frac{(O - E)^2}{E}$
Round-yellow seed	441	450	−9	81	0.18
Round-green seed	159	150	9	81	0.54
Wrinkled-yellow seed	143	150	−7	49	0.33
Wrinkled-green seed	57	50	7	49	0.98
	Σ 800				Σ 2.03

Expected frequencies calculated as follows:
Round-yellow seed = 9/16 x 800 = 450
Round-green seed = 3/16 x 800 = 150
Wrinkled-yellow seed = 3/16 x 800 = 150
Wrinkled-green seed = 1/16 x 800 = 50
χ^2 = 2.03
   (c) Degrees of freedom = (4-1) 3 .
   The critical value of χ^2 at P = 0.05 and at d.f.= 3 is 7.82. The calculated χ^2 is less than the critical value (2.03 < 7.82).

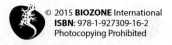

(d) We cannot reject H_0: There was no significant difference between the observed results and the expected phenotype ratio of 9:3:3:1. We must conclude that the genes controlling seed shape and colour are unlinked.

4. In both cases, we cannot reject H_0, but in the first case, the χ^2 value is much higher. In tomatoes, the genes for stem colour and leaf shape are on separate chromosomes, but given the relatively large χ^2 value, repeating the experiment with more plants, or replicates, would serve as a check.

127. Problems Involving Dihybrid Inheritance
(page 163)

1. (a)

	BL	Bl
Bl	BBLl	BBll
bl	BbLl	Bbll

Genotype ratio: 1BBLl: 1BBll: 1BbLl: 1Bbll
Phenotype ratio: 1 black short hair, 1: black long hair

(b)

	TL	Tl	tbL	tbl
tbL	TtbLL	TtbLl	tbtbLL	tbtbLl
tbl	TtbLl	Ttbll	tbtbLl	tbtbll

Genotype ratio:

1TtbLL : 2TtbLl : 1Ttbll : 1tbtbLL : 2tbtbLl : 1tbtbll
Phenotype ratio: 3: Tabby long hair, 1:Tabby short hair, 3: blotched tabby long hair, 1: blotched tabby short hair

2. (a) Self pollination of plants with orange striped flowers produces progeny in ratios close to 9:3:3:1 (the expected ratio of a cross between heterozygous offspring of true breeding parents). Thus you may hypothesise that O (orange petals) is dominant to o (yellow petals) and stripes (S) are dominant to no stripes (s).
   (b) The plants with the orange striped flowers were genotype OoSs. You know this because OoSs x OoSs will produce the progeny phenotypes in the observed 9:3:3:1 ratio.

3. (a) bbSS (brown/spotted) X BBss (solid/black) (which parent was male and which female is unknown. Parents must be homozygous since all the offspring are of one type: BbSs: black spotted).
   (b) F2 generation: BbSs X BbSs

	BS	Bs	bS	bs
BS	BBSS	BBSs	BbSS	BbSs
Bs	BBSs	BBss	BbSs	Bbss
bS	BbSS	BbSs	bbSS	bbSs
bs	BbSs	Bbss	bbSs	bbss

   (c) Spotted/black   9/16
       Spotted/brown   3/16
       Solid/black   3/16
       Solid/brown   1/16
       Ratio: 9:3:3:1 (described as above)

4. (a) F1: Genotype: all heterozygotes RrBb.
   (b) F1: Phenotype: all rough black coats.
   (c) F2 generation: RrBb X RrBb

	RB	Rb	rB	rb
RB	RRBB	RRBb	RrBB	RrBb
Rb	RRBb	RRbb	RrBb	Rrbb
rB	RrBB	RrBb	rrBB	rrBb
rb	RrBb	Rrbb	rrBb	rrbb

   (d) Rough/black 9/16   Smooth/black 3/16
       Rough/white 3/16   Smooth/white 1/16
       Ratio: 9:3:3:1 (described as above)

(e)

	RB	Rb	rB	rb
RB	RRBB	RRBb	RrBB	RrBb

(f) F2 Phenotype: all rough black coats.
(g) The parents' genotypes: RrBb X Rrbb

5. Note: Persian and Siamese parents are pedigrees (truebreeding) and homozygous for the genes involved.

   (a) Persian: UUss, Siamese: uuSS, Himalayan: uuss
   (b) F1: Genotype: all heterozygotes UuSs.
   (c) F1: Phenotype: all uniform colour, short haired.
   (d) F2 generation: UuSs X UuSs

	US	Us	uS	us
US	UUSS	UUSs	UuSS	UuSs
Us	UUSs	UUss	UuSs	Uuss
uS	UuSS	UuSs	uuSS	uuSs
us	UuSs	Uuss	uuSs	uuss

   (e) 1:15 or 1/16 uuss: Himalayan
   (f) Yes (only one type of allele combination is possible)
   (g) 3:13 or 3/16 (2 uuSs, 1 uuSS)

6. (a) Yes
   (b) Four phenotypes were produced. If there was no crossing over there would only be two phenotypes (parental types).
   (c) CucuEbeb, cucuebeb, Cucuebeb, cucuEbeb.

128. Gene Interactions (page 165)

1. (a) 9 walnut comb, 3 rose comb, 3 pea comb, 1 single comb.
   (b) Walnut comb
   (c) Single comb

2. (a) Colourless product
   (b) Colourless product
   (c) Purple product
   (d) Colourless product
   (e)

	AB	Ab
AB	AABB	AABb
Ab	AABb	AAbb
aB	AaBB	AaBb
ab	AaBb	Aabb

   3:1 purple to colourless

3. (a) GGYY, GgYY, GGYy, GgYy
   (b) ggYY, ggYy, GGyy, Ggyy, ggyy
   (c) Phenotypic ratio 9:7 Duplicate recessive epistasis

	GY	Gy	gY	gy
GY	GGYY	GGYy	GgYY	GgYy
Gy	GGYy	GGyy	GgYy	Ggyy
gY	GgYY	GgYy	ggYY	ggYy
gy	GgYy	Ggyy	ggYy	ggyy

4. Three colours are given, therefore the interaction must be **either recessive epistasis** or **dominant epistasis**.
   i. Any orange tailed fish crossed with any orange tailed fish produces only orange tailed fish. Therefore orange tailed fish could be (using the table) either BBhh or Bbhh, or bbHH, bbHh, or bbhh.
   ii. Red tailed fish must have dominant alleles because they produce all three colours when crossed with orange tailed fish (red is dominant to orange).
   iii. **Assuming the interaction is recessive epistasis** allows us to carry out crosses to test this. If we take BBhh to be orange or pink and bbHH to be pink or orange we get Bh

© 2015 **BIOZONE** International
ISBN: 978-1-927309-16-2
Photocopying Prohibited

x bH which gives BbHh - the heterozygote (red). Therefore the interaction cannot be recessive epistasis.

To check we can **assume the interaction is dominant epistasis**. In this case if we take bbHH to be orange or pink and bbhh to be pink or orange we get bH x bh which gives bbHh - all the same colour (either pink or orange). To double check we can cross bbHh with bbhh:

	bH	**bh**
bh	bbHh	bbhh

Two different genotypes are produced. From the table we can see that the homozygous recessive produces one colour and the genotype containing a heterozygote is a different colour. (50%, 50%). The observation can then **lead us to conclude that the gene interaction is dominant epistasis**.

---

129. Epistasis (page 167)

1. No. of phenotypes: 3

2. Black: B_C_ (a dominant allele for each gene)
   Brown: A dominant allele for gene C only (e.g. Ccbb)
   Albino: No dominant allele for gene C (e.g. ccBB, ccbb)

3.

Sperm

	BC	**Bc**	**bC**	**bc**
BC	BBCC Black	BBCc Black	BbCC Black	BbCc Black
Bc	BBCc Black	BBcc Albino	BbCc Black	Bbcc Albino
bC	BbCC Black	BbCc Black	bbCC Brown	bbCc Brown
bc	BbCc Black	Bbcc Albino	bbCc Brown	bbcc Albino

(Eggs)

Ratio: Black: brown: albino
        9 : 3 : 4

4. Homozygous albino (bbcc) x homozygous black (BBCC):
   Offspring genotype: 100% BbCc
   Offspring phenotype: 100% black

5. Homozygous brown (bbCC) x homozygous black (BBCC):
   Offspring genotype: 100% BbCC
   Offspring phenotype: 100% black

6. 4

7. Black: E_B_   Brown: E_bb   Yellow: eebb, eeB_

8. (a) All black, EeBb
   (b)

	EB	**Eb**	**eB**	**eb**
EB	EEBB black	EEBb black	EeBB black	EeBb black
Eb	EEBb black	EEbb brown	EeBb black	Eebb brown
eB	EeBB black	EeBb black	eeBB yellow (black nose)	eeBb yellow (black nose)
eb	EeBb black	Eebb brown	eeBb yellow (black nose)	eebb yellow (brown nose)

   (c) Collaboration (9:3:3:1)

9. (a) eeBb, eeBB
   (b) eebb
   (c) CCeeBb, CCeeBB

130. Polygenes (page 169)

1. Punnett square

Gametes	ABC	ABc	AbC	Abc	aBC	aBc	abC	abc
ABC	AABBCC	AABBCc	AABbCC	AABbCc	AaBBCC	AaBBCc	AaBbCC	AaBbCc
ABc	AABBCc	AABBcc	AABbCc	AABbcc	AaBBCc	AaBBcc	AaBbCc	AaBbcc
AbC	AABbCC	AABbCc	AAbbCC	AAbbCc	AaBbCC	AaBbCc	AabbCC	AabbCc
Abc	AABbCc	AABbcc	AAbbCc	AAbbcc	AaBbCc	AaBbcc	AabbCc	Aabbcc
aBC	AaBBCC	AaBBCc	AaBbCC	AaBbCc	aaBBCC	aaBBCc	aaBbCC	aaBbCc
aBc	AaBBCc	AaBBcc	AaBbCc	AaBbcc	aaBBCc	aaBBcc	aaBbCc	aaBbcc
abC	AaBbCC	AaBbCc	AabbCC	AabbCc	aaBbCC	aaBbCc	aabbCC	aabbCc
abc	AaBbCc	AaBbcc	AabbCc	Aabbcc	aaBbCc	aaBbcc	aabbCc	aabbcc

Darker skin	Same	Lighter skin

(a) 20   (b) 27.

2. Environmental influences will alter the colour of a person skin (such as tanning) to different extents.

3. Traits with continuous variation show a normal distribution curve when sampled and a graded variation in phenotype in the population. Such phenotypes are usually determined by a large number of genes and/or environmental influence. Examples include height, weight, hand span, foot size. In contrast, traits with discontinuous variation fall into one of a limited number of phenotypic variants and do not show a normal distribution curve when sampled. Differences in the phenotypes of individuals in a population are marked and do not grade into each other. Such phenotypes are usually controlled by a few different alleles at a few genes, e.g. chin cleft.

4. Student's own plot. Shape of the distribution is dependent on the data collected. The plot should show a statistically normal distribution if sample is representative of the population and large enough.
   (a) Calculations based on the student's own data.
   (b) Continuous distribution, normal distribution, or bell shaped curve are all acceptable answers if the data conform to this pattern.
   (c) Polygenic inheritance: Several (two or more) genes are involved in determining the phenotypic trait. Environment may also have an influence, especially if traits such as weight are chosen.
   (d) A large enough sample size (30+) provides sufficient data to indicate the distribution. The larger the sample size, the more closely one would expect the data plot to approximate the normal curve (assuming the sample was drawn from a population with a normal distribution for that attribute).

---

131. Chapter Review (page 171)
No model answer. Summary is the student's own.

132 KEY TERMS: Did You Get It? (page 172)

1.

Across	Down
2. Recombinant	1. Phenotype
9. Genotype	3. Meiosis
10. Codominance	4. Allele
13. Punnett square	5. Discontinuous
15. Dominant	6. Recessive
16. Trait	7. Continuous
17. Locus	8. Test cross
18. Homozygous	11. Back cross
19. Heterozygous	12. Multiple
	14. Linkage

2. Mutations are the ultimate... ...source of new alleles.
Alleles are variations... ...of a gene.
A person carrying two of the same alleles (one on each homologous chromosome)... ...is said to be homozygous for that gene.
If the person carries two different alleles... ...for the gene, they are heterozygous.
Alleles may be... ...dominant or recessive
A dominant allele... ...always expresses its trait whether it is in the homozygous or heterozygous condition.
A recessive allele only... ...expresses its trait if it is homozygous.

---

133. Small Flies and Giant Buttercups (page 174)

1. When the original species of drosophilidae arrived on the Hawaiian islands it found many new unoccupied niches into which it expanded, resulting in a extensive adaptive radiation.

2. The fruit flies are of interest because there are so many closely related species within a small area and speciation has been relatively frequent. The flies also have a relatively simple genome, making genetic studies relatively easy.

3. In general the oldest species of flies are found on the oldest islands. As islands appeared out of the sea the flies spread to new environments and diversified, giving rise to newer species.

4. Buttercups living in alpine areas periodically have their habitats reduced and their range restricted during periods of climatic warming. This restricts gene flow and leads to speciation. Periods of cooling allow for the expansion of their range and movement to new environments as well as hybridisation to form new species. Repeated many times, these cycles lead to a large range of species.

---

134. Gene Pools and Evolution (page 175)

1. & 2. **Note**: Do not include the beetle about to enter Deme 1 (aa) but include the beetle about to leave Deme 1 (Aa). For the purpose of the exercise, assume that the individual with the mutation **A'A** in Deme 1 is a normal **AA**.

Deme 1: 22 beetles   Deme 2: 19 beetles

Deme 1		Number counted	%
Allele types	A	26	59.1
	a	18	40.9
Allele combinations	AA	8	36.4
	Aa	10	45.4
	aa	4	18.2

Deme 2		Number counted	%
Allele types	A	13	34.2
	a	25	65.8
Allele combinations	AA	1	5.3
	Aa	11	57.9
	aa	7	36.8

---

3. (a) **Population size**: Large population acts as a 'buffer' for random, directional changes in allele frequencies. A small population can exhibit changes in allele frequencies because of random loss of alleles (failure of an individual to contribute young to the next generation).

(b) **Mate selection**: Random mating occurs in many animals and most plants. With 'mate selection', there is no random meeting of gametes, and certain combinations come together at a higher frequency than would occur by chance alone. This will alter the frequency of alleles in subsequent generations.

(c) **Gene flow between populations**: Immigration (incoming) and emigration (outgoing) has the effect of adding or taking away alleles from a population that can change allele frequencies. In some cases, two-way movements may cancel, with no net effect.

(d) **Mutations**: A source of new alleles. Most mutations are harmful, confer poor fitness, and will be lost from the gene pool over a few generations. Some may be neutral, conferring no advantage over organisms with different alleles. Occasionally, mutations may confer improved fitness and will increase in frequency with each generation, at the expense of other alleles.

(e) **Natural selection**: Selection pressures will affect some allele types more than others, causing allele frequencies to change with each generation.

4. (a) Increase genetic variation: Gene flow (migration), large population size, mutation.

(b) Decrease genetic variation: Natural selection, non-random mating (mate selection), genetic drift.

---

135. Changes in a Gene Pool (page 177)

1. This exercise (a)-(c) demonstrates how the allele frequencies change as different events take place:

Phase 1: Initial gene pool

This is the gene pool before any of the events take place:

	A	a	AA	Aa	aa
No.	27	23	7	13	5
%	54	46	28	52	20

Phase 2: Natural selection

The population is now reduced by 2 to 23. The removal of two homozygous recessive individuals has altered the allele combination frequencies (rounding errors occur).

	A	a	AA	Aa	aa
No.	27	19	7	13	3
%	58.7	41.3	30.4	56.5	13.0

Phase 3: Immigration / emigration

The addition of dominant alleles and the loss of recessive alleles makes further changes to the allele frequencies.

	A	a	AA	Aa	aa
No.	29	17	8	13	2
%	63	37	34.8	56.5	8.7

136. Hardy-Weinberg Calculations (page 178)

1. **Working:** q= 0.1, p= 0.9, q^2= 0.01, p^2= 0.81, 2pq= 0.18
   Proportion of black offspring = 2pq + p^2 x 100% = 99%;
   Proportion of grey offspring = q^2 x 100% = 1%

2. **Working:** q= 0.3, p= 0.7, q^2= 0.09, p^2= 0.49, 2pq= 0.42
   (a) Frequency of tall (dominant) gene (allele): 70%
   (b) 42% heterozygous; 42% of 400 = **168**

3. **Working:** q= 0.6, p= 0.4, q^2= 0.36, p^2= 0.16, 2pq= 0.48
   (a) 40% dominant allele
   (b) 48% heterozygous; 48% of 1000 = **480**.

4. **Working:** q= 0.2, p= 0.8, q^2= 0.04, p^2= 0.64, 2pq= 0.32
   (a) 32% heterozygous (carriers)
   (b) 80% dominant allele

5. **Working:** q= 0.5, p= 0.5, q^2= 0.25, p^2= 0.25, 2pq= 0.5
   Proportion of population that becomes white = 25%

6. **Working:** q= 0.8, p= 0.2, q^2= 0.64, p^2= 0.04, 2pq =0.32
   (a) 80%   (c) 36%   (e) 96%
   (b) 32%   (d) 4%

7. **Working:** q= 0.1, p= 0.9, q^2= 0.01, p^2= 0.81, 2pq= 0.18
   Proportion of people expected to be albino (i.e. proportion that are homozygous recessive) = 1%

137. Analysis of a Squirrel Gene Pool (page 180)

1. Graph of population changes:

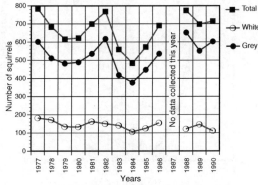

(a) 784 to 484 = 61% fluctuation
(b) Total population numbers exhibit an oscillation with a period of 5-6 years (2 cycles shown). Fluctuations occur in both grey and albino populations.

2. Graph of genotype changes:

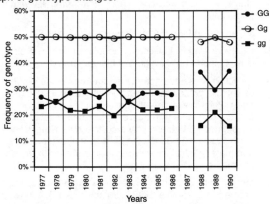

(a) GG genotype: Relatively constant frequency until the last 3-4 years, which show an increase. Possibly an increase over the total sampling period.
(b) Gg genotype: Uniform frequency.
(c) gg genotype: Relatively constant frequency until the last 3-4 years which exhibit a decline. Possibly a decrease over the total sampling period.

3. Graph of allele changes:

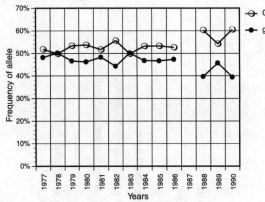

(a) Frequency of G: Increases in the last 3-4 years.
(b) Frequency of g: Decreases in the last 3-4 years.

4. (a) The *frequency of alleles* graph (to a lesser extent the *frequency of genotypes* graph)
   (b) Changes in allele frequencies in a population provide the best indication of significant evolutionary changes occurring. These cannot be deduced simply from changes in numbers or genotypes.

5. There are at least two possible causes (any one of):
   – Genetic drift in a relatively small population, i.e. there are random changes in allele frequencies as a result of small population size.
   – Natural selection against albinos. Albinism represents a selective disadvantage in terms of survival and reproduction (albinos are more vulnerable to predators because of greater visibility and lower fitness).

138. Natural Selection (page 182)

1. Stable environments favour the most common phenotypes. Environmental instability provides a chance that extreme phenotypes might be advantageous, but in a stable environment, this is unlikely to happen. Predictability encourages a reduction in phenotypic variability because this is no disadvantage when the environment is largely static.

2. (a) Drought favoured birds with beak sizes at two extremes of the range, since these birds could exploit the small and the large seed sizes.
   (b) Continuation of the drought could lead to further divergence in beak size.
   (c) The selection pressures favouring a bimodal distribution in beak size would be reduced and medium sized beaks would become relatively more common (i.e. there would be a shift from disruptive to stabilising selection).

139. Directional Selection in Darwin's Finches
(page 183)

1. (a)

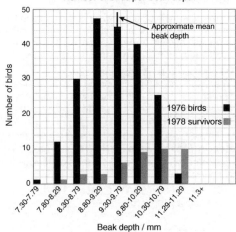

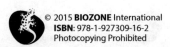

(b)

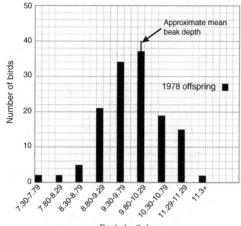

Number of birds per beak depth

Approximate mean beak depth

1978 offspring ■

2. (a) See graphs above.
   (b) Approximately 0.5 mm
   (c) Yes, beak depth is heritable. If the drought continues the population may become increasingly dominated by individuals with deeper beaks. Smaller beak sizes will become increasingly rare or absent.

3. Smaller seeds were probably eaten first (as beaks were smaller). This left the birds competing for larger seeds such that birds with larger beaks were more successful and were more likely to survive.

140. Directional Selection in Moths (page 184)

1. The appearance of the wings and body (how speckled and how dark the pigmentation).

2. The selection pressure (the differential effect of selective predation on survival) changed from favouring the survival of light coloured forms in the unpolluted environments (prior to the Industrial Revolution) to favouring the dark morph (over the light morph) during the Industrial Revolution (when there was a lot of soot pollution). In more recent times, with air quality improving, the survival of the light coloured forms has once again improved.

3. As the frequency of the M allele increased so did the frequency of the dark form. Similarly as the frequency of the m allele decreased so did the grey morph.

4. The frequency of the darker form fell from 95% to 50%.

141. Disruptive Selection in Darwin's Finches (page 185)

1. (a) Large and small seeds became relatively more abundant.
   (b) The change in the relative abundance of seed sizes produced a negative selection pressure on finches with intermediate sized beaks. Those with smaller and larger beaks fared better during the drought because they could exploit the smaller and larger seed sizes.

2. Beak size determines fitness, which shows a bimodal distribution. Birds with small beaks (-1.0 single measure) or larger beaks (single measure 1.25) show higher fitness (leave more offspring) than birds with intermediate beak sizes.

3. (a) Mate selection is non-random.
   (b) The graph shows that birds tend to choose mates with a similar beak size. This relationship is stronger when the environmental conditions are more extreme and weaker in more moderate conditions.

142. Selection for Human Birth Weight (page 186)

Sample data: Use the data below if students are unable to collect from local sources.

3.740	3.830	3.530	3.095	3.630
1.560	3.910	4.180	3.570	2.660
3.150	3.400	3.380	2.660	3.375
3.840	3.630	3.810	2.640	3.955
2.980	3.350	3.780	3.260	4.510
3.800	4.170	4.400	3.770	3.400
3.825	3.130	3.400	3.260	4.100
3.220	3.135	3.090	3.830	3.970
3.840	4.710	4.050	4.560	3.350
3.380	3.690	1.495	3.260	3.430
3.510	3.230	3.570	3.620	3.260
3.315	3.230	3.790	2.620	3.030
3.350	3.970	3.915	2.040	4.050
3.105	3.790	3.060	2.770	3.400
1.950	3.800	2.390	2.860	4.110
1.970	3.800	4.490	2.640	3.550
4.050	4.220	2.860	4.060	3.740
4.082	3.000	3.230	2.800	4.050
4.300	3.030	3.160	3.300	2.350
3.970	2.980	3.550	3.070	2.715

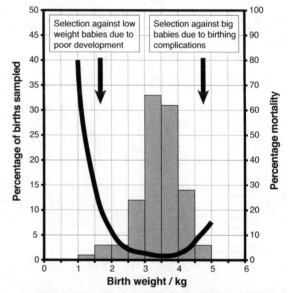

Selection against low weight babies due to poor development

Selection against big babies due to birthing complications

Note: For the construction of weight classes, it is necessary to have a range of weight categories that do not overlap. The data collected should be sorted into weight classes of: 0.0-0.49, 0.50-0.99, 1.0-1.49, 1.5-1.99, etc.

1. Normal distribution (bell-shaped curve), probably with a skew to the left.

2. 3.5 kg (taken from the table: only 2% mortality)

3. Good correlation. Lowest frequencies of surviving birth weights correspond to birth weights of highest mortality.

4. Selection pressures operate at extremes of the range: premature babies have reduced survival because their body systems are not fully developed; large babies present problems with delivery as the birth canal can only accommodate babies up to a certain size. **Note**: Very large babies can occur as the result of gestational diabetes. Before adequate medical intervention, this often led to the death of the mother and/or the baby.

5. Medical intervention can now allow babies that are very premature to survive (babies as small as 1.5 kg have a good chance of survival today, but this has not historically been the case). Caesarean deliveries have also allowed larger babies to be born. **Note**: This technology is available to wealthy societies thereby reducing the effect of this selection pressure. Developing countries still experience this selection pressure.

143. Natural Selection in Pocket Mice (page 187)

1. (a) DD, Dd   (b) dd

2. See column graphs above

3. (a) The dark mice are found on the dark rocks.
   (b) Dark mice are found on the dark rocks as they blend in

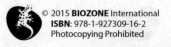
© 2015 **BIOZONE** International
ISBN: 978-1-927309-16-2
Photocopying Prohibited

Percentage reflectance of rock pocket mice coats

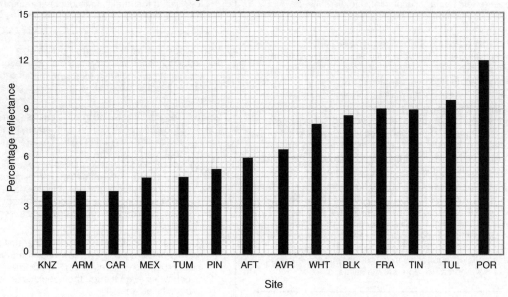

Percentage reflectance of rocks

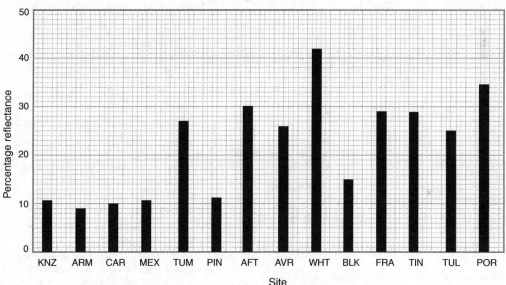

better, making it harder for predators to spot them. Dark mice on light rocks would be easily seen by predators. The same applies for light mice and dark rocks.

(c) The mice at BLK and WHT do not conform to this generalisation. The mice at BLK are lighter than predicted from the lower rock reflectance and the mice at WHT are darker than predicted from the higher rock reflectance.

(d) These mice might represent a recent migration to those areas from mostly dark or light population. There has not been enough time for the population to evolve to match their surroundings.

4. Dark colour has evolved at least twice in rock pocket mice populations.

144. Selection for Skin Colour in Humans (page 189)

1. (a) Folate is essential for healthy neural development. Explanatory note: A deficiency causes (usually fatal) neural tube defects (e.g. spina bifida).

(b) Vitamin D is required for the absorption of dietary calcium and normal skeletal development. Explanatory note: A deficiency causes rickets in children or osteomalacia in adults. Osteomalacia in pregnancy can lead to pelvic fractures and inability to carry a pregnancy to term.

2. (a) Skin cancer normally develops after reproductive age and

therefore protection against it provides no reproductive advantage and so no mechanism for selection.

(b) The new hypothesis for the evolution of skin colour links the skin colour-UV correlation directly to evolutionary fitness (reproductive success). Skin needs to be dark enough to protect folate stores from destruction by UV and so prevent fatal neural defects in the offspring. However it also needs to be light enough to allow enough UV to penetrate the skin in order to manufacture vitamin D for calcium absorption. Without this, the female skeleton cannot successfully support a pregnancy. Because these pressures act on individuals both before and during reproductive age they provide a mechanism for selection. The balance of opposing selective pressures determines eventual skin colouration.

3. Women have a higher requirement for calcium during pregnancy and lactation. Calcium absorption is dependent on vitamin D, making selection pressure on females for lighter skins greater than for males.

4. The Inuit people have such abundant vitamin D in their diet that the selection pressure for lighter skin (for UV absorption and vitamin D synthesis) is reduced and their skin can be darker.

5. (a) Higher chances of getting rickets or (the adult equivalent) osteomalacia due to low UV absorption.

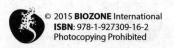

(b) The simplest option to avoid these problems is for these people to take dietary supplements to increase the amount of vitamin D they obtain.

146. Modelling Natural Selection (page 193)

There is no set answer to this activity. Students should notice that the phenotypes that stand out from the background become reduced in number over time.

147. Genetic Drift (page 194)

1. (a) Genetic drift is the random changes in allele frequencies in populations which are unrelated to natural selection.
   (b) The effect of genetic drift is more pronounced in smaller populations than larger populations because of the relative size of the gene pools.

2. Genetic drift has a relatively greater effect in small populations and can result in the loss or fixation of alleles relatively rapidly. These changes can accumulate to a point that speciation occurs. Explanatory note: Unlike natural selection, genetic drift is a stochastic (random) process, and the changes due to genetic drift are not driven by environmental pressures. Changes in allele frequencies may therefore be beneficial, neutral, or detrimental to reproductive success.

148. The Founder Effect (page 195)

1.

Mainland	Nos	%		Nos	%
Allele A	48	54.5	Black	37	84
Allele a	40	45.5	Pale	7	16
Total	88	100			
Island	Nos	%		Nos	%
Allele A	12	75	Black	8	100
Allele a	4	25	Pale	0	0
Total	16	100			

2. The frequency of the dominant allele (A) is higher on the island population.

3. (a) Plants: Seeds are carried by wind, birds and water
   (b) Animals: Reach islands largely by 'rafting' - situation where animals are carried offshore while clinging to vegetation; some animals survive better than others
   (c) Non-marine birds: Blown off course and out to sea by a storm. Birds with strong stamina may survive.

4. Block A % for MDH-1 a in order 1-15: 61, 61, 64, 58, 61, 53, 68, 58, 56, 58, 56, 50, 50, 62, 25

   Block B % MDH-1 a in order 1-13: 19, 39, 25, 32, 30, 39, 30, 40, 42, 39, 46, 46, 53

5. Snails, although mobile, are restricted by their need for moisture. The tarmac roads and open areas on the blocks make movement between the two populations difficult as are they are open and generally dry areas.

6. The frequencies have become different through a possible founder effect in which the original populations in each block had slightly different allele frequencies to begin with, or random events (i.e. genetic drift) have altered the proportion of alleles being passed to the next generation. Although adjacent, selection pressures in the blocks could also have been subtly different. It is likely that all these processes have contributed to the differences in allele frequencies.

7. Colony 15

149. Genetic Bottlenecks (page 197)

1. A sudden decrease in the size of a population can result in a corresponding reduction in genetic variation. This means the population has few 'genetic resources' to cope with the selection pressures imposed on it. In particular, it manifests itself as reduced reproductive success and a greater sensitivity to disease.

2. Poor genetic diversity means that if one individual is susceptible to a disease, then they are all likely to be vulnerable, a direct result of reduced genetic diversity.

3. With reduced genetic diversity, selection pressures on the population are likely to have devastating effects on survival if

one trait proves unfavourable. Since all cheetahs are virtually identical in their traits, individuals are similarly vulnerable and respond similarly to the same selection pressure.

150. Isolation and Species Formation (page 198)

1. Isolating mechanisms protect the gene pool from the diluting and potentially adverse effects of introduced genes. Species are well adapted to their niche; foreign genes will usually reduce fitness.

2. (a) Geographical isolation physically separates populations (and gene pools) but, if reintroduced, the two populations could potentially interbreed, i.e. reproductive isolation may not have occurred.
   (b) Geographical isolation enables populations to diverge in response to different selection pressures and (potentially) develop reproductive isolating mechanisms. Reproductive isolation won't generally occur in a populations in which there is gene flow (unless by special events such as polyploidy).

3. Geographical isolation physically separates populations (gene pools) so there is no gene flow between them. Ecological isolation arises as a result of different preferences in habitat or behaviour even though the populations occupy the same geographical area.

151. Reproductive Isolation (page 199)

1. (a) Postzygotic: hybrid breakdown
   (b) Prezygotic: structural
   (c) Prezygotic: temporal
   (d) Postzygotic: hybrid inviability

2. They are a secondary backup if the first isolating mechanism fails. The majority of species do not interbreed because of prezygotic mechanisms. Postzygotic mechanisms are generally rarer events.

152. Allopatric Speciation (page 201)

1. Animals may move into new environments to reduce competition for resources or because a new habitat becomes available (loss of geographical barrier or loss of another species freeing up an existing niche).

2. Plants move by dispersing their seeds.

3. Gene flow between the parent population and dispersing populations is regular.

4. Cooler periods (glacials) result in a drop in sea level as more water is stored as ice. As the temperature increases, the ice will begin to melt, and sea level will rise. The variation in sea level will depend on how much water is stored and released in response to the temperature change.

5. (a) Physical barriers that could isolate populations include the formation of mountain ranges, the formation of rivers or their change of course, the expansion or formation of desert, the advance of ice sheets, glacial retreat (isolating alpine adapted populations), and sea level rise. On a longer time scale, the formation of seas as a result of continental drift can isolate populations too.
   (b) Emigration (leaving one area and moving to another) will potentially reduce the genetic diversity of both gene pools, the migrants and the parent population. Depending on the extent of the migration, the effect will be the same as geographical isolation. The allele frequencies of the two isolates will diverge.

6. (a) The selection pressures on an isolated population may be quite different for that of the parent population. The immediate physical environment (e.g. temperature, wind exposure) as well as climatic region (e.g. temperate to tropical) may differ, as will biotic factors, such as competition, predation, and disease. In a different region, the food type and availability is also likely to different for the two populations. The shift in selection pressures may result in changes in allele frequencies as those best adapted to the new conditions survive to reproduce.
   (b) Some individuals in the isolated population will have allele

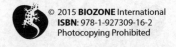

combinations (and therefore a phenotype) that better suits the unique set of selection pressures at the new location. Over a period of time (generations) certain alleles for a gene will become more common in the gene pool, at the expense of other less suited alleles.

7. Reproductive isolation could develop in geographically isolated populations through the development of prezygotic and then postzygotic barriers to breeding. Prezygotic isolation would probably begin with ecological isolation, e.g. habitat preferences in the isolated population would diverge from the parent population in the new environment. Prezygotic isolating mechanisms that could develop subsequently to prevent successful mating include temporal isolation (e.g. seasonal shifts in the timing of breeding), incompatible behaviours (e.g. different mating rituals), and structural incompatibilities (e.g. incompatible mating apparatus). Gamete mortality (failure of egg and sperm to unite) can also prevent formation of the zygote in individuals that manage to copulate successfully. Once prezygotic isolation is established, post-zygotic mechanisms such as zygote mortality (in which the fertilised egg dies), reduced fertility in the hybrid, or hybrid breakdown (e.g. sterile F_2) increase the isolation of the new species and prevent gene flow between it and the parent species.

8. Sympatric species are closely related species whose distribution overlaps. Allopatric species are species that remain geographically separated.

153. Stages in Species Development (page 203)
1. Some butterflies rested on top of boulders, others rested in the grass.

2. Selection pressure on BSBs is the need to maintain operating body temperature at the high altitude (fitness is higher when they can efficiently absorb heat from boulders). Selection pressure on the GSBs is probably predation as these lowland butterflies survive better where they can avoid detection.

154. Sympatric Speciation (page 204)
1. Sympatric speciation describes a speciation event that occurs without geographical separation. The two species are separated by some other means, such as niche differentiation or a spontaneous chromosomal change (polyploidy).

2. Polyploidy creates extra sets of chromosomes for an individual that make it impossible for it to reproduce with members of its parental population. Hybrids may form but they will be sterile.

3. Modern wheat, also seedless watermelons, kiwifruit

4. If two groups within a species population have slightly different habitats and food or foraging preferences (niche differentiation), then they will not come into contact for mating.

155. Selective Breeding in Animals (page 205)
1. (a) Selective breeding is the process by which humans select organisms with desirable traits and breed then together so the trait appears reliably in the next generation.
   (b) Selective breeding is able to produce specific, useful traits in an organism that can be reliably passed on.

2. (a) Good eyesight and sense of smell. An ability to corner and hold prey without necessarily killing it.
   (b) Low aggression to stock, obedience, ability to anticipate the behaviour of stock animals and respond to stock movements, bark and use body language to direct stock movement, protect stock from predators.
   (c) Pet dogs generally have puppy-like qualities throughout their life. They are relaxed, highly sociable, easy to train and play with, and are seldom aggressive.
   (d) Aggressive behaviour to strangers, excellent hearing and sense of smell, alert to intruders, respond by barking.

3. Student responses required and will vary depending on what they regard as important.

156. Selection in Livestock (page 206)
1. Selection causes rapid changes because only organisms with desirable traits are allowed to breed. This both eliminates

undesirable traits and increases the proportion of offspring with desirable traits. Continued focus on particular traits results in their rapid spread through the population with each generation, until certain traits become fixed.

2. The dairy industry uses specific bulls to fertilise thousands of cows, producing thousands of calves with desirable traits. The industry spends millions of dollars on breeding programmes that select only the best genetic profiles for breeding.

157. Selection and Population Change (page 207)
1. (a) As milk yield in Holstein cows increases fertility decreases.
   (b) It suggests the genes for high milk yield and low fertility (or low milk yield and high fertility) are carried on the same chromosome (linked) and are very close together so that no crossing over and recombination occurs.

2. Milk yield will ultimately be limited by fertility (very high yield cows will have lower fertility and produce fewer offspring).

3. The sire must carry the genes for the desirable traits, as these will be inherited by his daughters. In addition, one sire has enormous influence as he potentially services many females (through artificial insemination).

4. Selective breeding is an artificial form of natural selection usually based around the improvement of one or two traits desired by humans, in this case high milk yield. Natural selection favours traits that will increase reproductive success but this may result in a compromise (best balance) between correlated (genetically linked) traits, e.g. milk production and offspring production (fertility) are both costly in terms of energy expenditure so in nature there will be a balance. Humans have selected for milk yield over fertility to the detriment of the latter (probably because low fertility can be overcome with the use of administered hormones and other reproductive technologies).

158. Selective Breeding in Crop Plants (page 208)
1. (a) Cauliflower: flowers
   (b) Kale: leaf
   (c) Broccoli: inflorescence
   (d) Brussels sprout: lateral buds
   (e) Cabbage: apical (terminal) bud
   (f) Kohlrabi: stem (swollen)

2. If allowed to flower, all six can cross-pollinate.

3. Broccoli is an inflorescence, therefore breeders would have selected for plants exhibiting clumps of many small flowers. They would also have selected for plants producing thick fleshy flower buds. These two main characteristics, selected together over generations of plants, eventually produced modern broccoli.

4. (a) Students may choose a variety of traits including (for example) uniform fruit size or colour, uniform tree shape, sweet fruit, with crisp, juicy flesh, fruit that remains on the tree until ripe, fruit that stores well, etc.
   (b) Method to establish this trait must be described: e.g. desired trait is identified. Plants with this trait are bred together. Offspring with the trait are selected for breeding. This happens for many generations until the trait is established satisfactorily (fixed).

5. (a) Selective breeding for specific traits generally reduces genetic diversity by increasing homozygosity in the offspring. When selection is focussed on specific traits, other phenotypes (therefore genotypes) are rejected and their genes are lost from the gene pool. This is particularly the case when the genes for desirable traits are associated, e.g. a genotype for heavy fruiting might also be associated (e.g. through linkage) with lower seed production. Selection for one trait will then also select for another.
   (b) Retention of genetic diversity is particularly important in crop plants because it provides a pool of genes from which to improve strains and guard against loss of adaptability in crops. In terms of food security, it is dangerous to rely on only a restricted number of strains for most of our food. A good example is the Irish potato

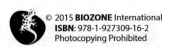

famine where potatoes were the main food crop and farmers relied almost exclusively on one high yielding potato variety. When this variety proved vulnerable to blight, most of the country's crop was lost and there was a huge famine. The country lost food security by relying on one variety and by not having a readily available store of diversity on which to draw.

6.   Cultivated American cotton would have originated from the interspecific hybridisation of Old World cotton and wild American cotton.

7.   Cavendish bananas do not produce seed and therefore must be reproduced by asexual propagation. As a result, all Cavendish banana plants are genetically identical and all will be vulnerable to the Panama disease strain. Moreover, because the plant is sterile, it is not possible to breed into it any more genetic diversity and it will not be able to naturally produce resistance to the disease within the population (except perhaps in the unlikely event of a favourable mutation).

8.   Wild plants and ancient breeds possess alleles that may have been lost from inbred lines. The retention of these ancient cultivars provides a gene bank and a buffer of genetic diversity which can be used to improve the inbred cultivars in the future.

159. Breeding Modern Wheat (page 210)

1.   Any three of the following:
     Large grain size, high gluten (protein) content, high yield, less tendency for stalks to break, disease resistance, non-shattering heads.

2.   The evolution of modern wheat involved two natural hybridisation events accompanied by polyploidy to restore fertility. These events produced Emmer and common wheat, which were selected under cultivation for increased yield, pest and disease resistance, and high protein content. Recent selection techniques have enabled these desirable traits to be tagged to markers, which increases the efficiency of the selection process and ensures the selection process (the gain towards the desirable phenotype) proceeds more rapidly.

160. Chapter Review (page 211)

No model answer. Summary is the student's own.

161. KEY TERMS: Did You Get It? (page 212)

1.   allopatric speciation (H), founder effect (I), gene flow (G), gene pool (C), genetic bottleneck (B), genetic drift (L), Hardy-Weinberg principle (J), natural selection (A), polyploidy (M), reproduction isolation (K), selective breeding (D), speciation (E), sympatric speciation (F)

2.   Directional selection describes the situation where a phenotype at one extreme of the phenotypic range has the greatest fitness, so the phenotypic norm shifts in the direction of that phenotype, e.g. selection for dark morphs of *Biston* moths in England during the Industrial Revolution. Stabilising selection describes the situation where fitness is highest for the most common phenotype and there is selection against phenotypes at the extremes of the phenotypic range, e.g. selection for human birth weight.

3.   (a) Recessive (bb) = 40%. bb = q^2 = 0.4.
          q = $\sqrt{0.4}$ = 0.63.
          p = 1- q = 0.37
          2pq (heterozygous) = 2 x 0.63 x 0.37 = 0.47 = 47%
     (b) p^2 = 0.37^2 = 0.14

4.   (a) M = $\sqrt{0.49}$ = 0.7
     (b) N = $\sqrt{0.09}$ = 0.3 (or q = 1- p = 1 - 0.7 = 0.3)

163. DNA Amplification Using PCR (page 215)

1.   To produce large quantities of 'cloned' DNA from very small samples. Large quantities are needed for effective analysis. Very small quantities are often unusable.

2.   Detail not necessarily required in the answer bracketed. A double stranded DNA is heated (to 98°C for 5 min), causing

the two strands to separate. Primers, free nucleotides, and DNA polymerase are added to the sample. The sample is then cooled (to 60°C for a few minutes), and the primers anneal to the DNA strands. The sample is incubated and complementary strands are created (by the DNA polymerase) using each strand of the DNA sample as a template. The process is repeated about 25 times, each time the number of templates doubles over the previous cycle.

3.   (a) Forensic samples taken at the scene of a crime (e.g. hair, blood, semen).
     (b) Archaeological samples from early human remains.
     (c) Samples taken from the remains of prehistoric organisms mummified or preserved in ice, amber, or tar pits etc.

4.   This exercise can be done on a calculator by pressing the 1 button (for the original sample) and then multiplying by 2 repeatedly (to simulate each cycle).
     (a) 1024   (b) 33 554 432   (33.5 million)

5.   (a) It would be amplified along with the intended DNA sample, contaminating the sample and rendering it unusable.
     (b) Sources of contamination (any two of):
          Dirty equipment (equipment that has DNA molecules left on it from previous treatments).
          DNA from the technician (dandruff from the technician is a major source of contamination!)
          Spores, viruses and bacteria in the air.
     (c) Precautions to avoid contamination (any two of):
          Using disposable equipment (pipette tips, gloves).
          Wearing a **head cover** (disposable cap).
          Use of **sterile procedures**.
          Use of **plastic disposable tubes with caps** that seal the contents from air contamination.

6.   (a) and (b) any of the following procedures require a certain minimum quantity of DNA in order to be useful: DNA sequencing, gene cloning, DNA profiling, transformation, making artificial genes. Descriptions of these procedures are provided in the workbook

164. Gel Electrophoresis (page 217)

1.   Purpose: To separate mixtures of molecules (proteins, nucleic acids) on the basis of size, electric charge and other physical properties.

2.   (a) The frictional (retarding) force of each fragment's size (larger fragments travel more slowly than smaller ones).
     (b) The strength of the electric field (movement is more rapid in a stronger field). Note: The temperature and ionic strength of the buffer can be varied to optimise separation of the fragments.

3.   The gel is full of pores (holes) through which the fragments must pass. Smaller fragments pass through these pores more easily than larger ones.

165. Interpreting Electrophoresis Gels (page 218)

1.   (a) and (b)
     Cow synthesised DNA:
     TGA TTG TAA GCT TTC AGG GTG GGT GAT TA
     Cow sample DNA:
     ACT AAC ATT CGA AAG TCC CAC CCA CTA AT

     Sheep synthesised DNA:
     TAG TTG TAG GCT TTT TGG GTG GGT GAT TA
     Sheep sample DNA:
     ATC AAC ATC CGA AAA ACC CAC CCA CTA AT

     Goat synthesised DNA:
     TGG TTG TAG GCT TTC TGG GTG GGT AAT TA
     Goat sample DNA:
     ACC AAC ATC CGA AAG ACC CAC CCA TTA AT

     Horse synthesised DNA:
     TGT TTG TAG GCC TTT AGA GTG GGT GAT TA
     Horse sample DNA:
     ACA AAC ATC CGG AAA TCT CAC CCA CTA AT

     (c) Sheep and goat (3 differences)
     (d) Goat and horse (6 differences)

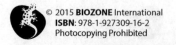

© 2015 **BIOZONE** International
ISBN: 978-1-927309-16-2

2.

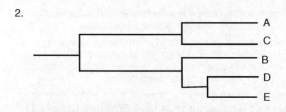

166. The Principles of DNA Sequencing (page 219)
1. (a) A dideoxyribonucleic acid
   (b) and (c)

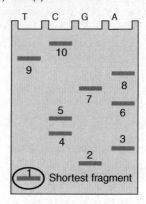

(d) T G A C C A G A T C
(e) A C T G G T C T A G

2. A reaction vessel is needed for each modified base. If all the modified bases were put in the same vessel there would be no way of distinguishing between them once placed on an electrophoresis gel.

3. 1% modified DNA is enough to produced terminated DNA fragments but is a small enough to allow other non-modified DNA to be incorporated in the DNA fragment. Too much modified DNA would cause termination of DNA replication too early in too many cases.

167. Advancements in DNA Sequencing (page 220)
1. (a) In next generation sequencing, the complementary DNA bases are read as they are attached to the DNA strand. In first generation sequencing lengths of DNA are read on a gel or by a laser after they have been produced.
   (b) Third generation sequencers read the DNA sequence base by base as the operation is proceeding without the need for nucleotides with fluorescent tags.
   (c) The sequencing devices have become physically smaller, making them easier to transport or even use in the field.

2. (a) Bioinformatics is the storage, retrieval, and analysis of biological information.
   (b) Bioinformatics has allowed scientists to store and quickly access and analyse many different DNA sequences from many different organisms. The ability to directly compare sequence information from multiple genomes has lead to greater understanding of evolutionary relationships.

168. Genome Projects (page 222)
1 (a) 49.67 times bigger
   (b) 652.2 times smaller
   (c) 18,750 times smaller

2. Large genomes require a lot of resources to replicate, thus reproduction and growth rates are low and this increases the risk of extinction.

4. Sequencing the DNA of major crop plants gives information on the genetic basis of important characteristics, such as growth, yield, and disease resistance. This information can be used to improve productivity and breeding programmes.

169. Investigating Genetic Diversity (page 223)
1. The TV11-14 group forms a distinct clade, which branched before the genetically distinct TV1-10 group (which is part of another clade that includes the Cape Royds, Cape Evans, and Beaufort Island groups). The TV1-10 group forms a cluster that is genetically closer than the other groups in the clade with which it shares a common ancestor.

2. The fact that the two types do not interbreed is significant because it means that reproductive isolating mechanisms have developed, or are in the process of developing. The two types may already be distinct species, or they could be in the process of speciating (if physical separation of the groups is the primary factor preventing their interbreeding).

3. Gene flow between populations will be very limited, if it occurs at all, because the springtails have very limited motility and are likely to die if blown any distance.

4. These conditions would have been ideal for the development of two species from a common ancestor. Small populations, isolated on mountain tops on either side of the valley, are likely to have been genetically different by virtue of the founder effect, and would then may have been subjected to subtly different selection pressures (different microclimates etc.). The lack of gene flow (low dispersal), combined with the small population size, would have increased the effect of genetic drift in the isolated populations, which could then diverge genetically in a relatively short time.

170. The Human Genome Project (page 225)
1. The HGP aims to map the entire base sequence of every chromosome in the human cell (our genome), to identify all genes in the sequence, determine what they express (protein produced), and determine the precise role of every gene on the chromosomes.

2. A HapMap will allow researchers to find genes and genetic variations that affect health and disease. It will also be a powerful resource for studying the genetic factors contributing to variation in response to environment, susceptibility to infection, and responses to drugs and vaccines.

3. (a) Medical (any of the following):
   – Will identify the location and sequence for up to 4000 known genetic diseases, opening up opportunities for drug therapy.
   – Will provide the information to enable the production of human proteins to correct metabolic deficiencies.
   – Will open up the possibility of gene therapy for many genetic diseases.
   – Will enable the development of new therapeutic drugs to block metabolic pathways.
   – With greater knowledge, emphasis will shift from treatment of disease to better diagnosis and prevention of disease.
   – Screening for genetic predisposition to disease.
   – The ability to sequence quickly and directly will revolutionise mutation research (direct study of the link between mutagens and their effects).
   (b) Non-medical (any of the following):
   – What we learn about human genetics will enable improvement of livestock management.
   – Provides a knowledge base that is a key to understanding the structure, function, and organisation of DNA in chromosomes.
   – Provides the basis for comparative studies with other organisms (e.g. for taxonomic purposes).
   – Provides a greater understanding of human evolution and anthropology.
   – Facilitates developments in forensics.

4. (a) Proteomics is the study (including identification) of the protein products of identified genes.
   (b) Proteomics relies on the knowledge gained by the HGP, but will provide the most useful information by determining the biological function of the mapped genes. It will show us what genes do, which will have applications in the medical and pharmaceutical industries.

5. Student's own discussion. Suggestions for each issue listed in the table (pros and cons) are as follows:

© 2015 **BIOZONE** International
ISBN: 978-1-927309-16-2
Photocopying Prohibited

– Rights of third parties:
(a) They should have the genetic information in order to make an informed decisions (about insurance premiums etc.) to the benefit of those with "favourable" genetic test results.
(b) They should be denied the information because they could use it to unfairly discriminate against people with "unfavourable" genetic test results.

– No treatment, therefore the knowledge is pointless:
(a) Although there may be no treatment initially, treatment may become available and knowledge of genetic predisposition will allow informed decisions to be made at short notice if necessary.
(b) Knowing that one has a disease and cannot do anything about it could create emotional problems for many people.

– High costs of tests:
(a) Although the costs are high, the knowledge is important to a person's health and to medical research generally and is justifiable.
(b) If costs are not met by public funds, the high costs will preclude those individuals who cannot personally afford them.

– Genetic information is hereditary:
(a) Knowledge of an inherited disease or disorder lets family members assess their risks when planning their own lives.
(b) Family members may feel forced to not have children if their risk of an inherited disorder is high.

171. Screening for Genes (page 227)
1. A DNA probe allows a region of DNA to be marked and identified.

2. The DNA probe is a sequence of DNA that is complementary to the target region of DNA. It is therefore able to bond to the target DNA allowing that region to be identified.

3. Double stranded DNA must be denatured to a single strand so that the base pairs are exposed and the complementary base pairs on the DNA probe can bond to the target region.

4. Genes are visualised using fluorescent light or X-ray film, depending on the tag that has been added to the probe being used. The target DNA sequence will appear as a band on the electrophoresis gel.

172. Synthetic Genes (page 228)
1. (a) Synthetic DNA is constructed in the 3' to 5' direction, opposite to natural DNA synthesis.
(b) Oligonucleotides are used to prevent the DNA bases incorrectly bonding to each other (the longer the chain the more chance of incorrect DNA bonding).

2. New genes that do not exist in nature may be produced. These may be used to produce new materials for industry or new therapeutic drugs.

173. DNA Profiling Using PCR (page 229)
1. STRs (microsatellites) are non-coding nucleotide sequences (2-6 base pairs long) that repeat themselves many times over (repeats of up to 100X). The human genome has numerous different STRs; equivalent sequences in different people vary considerably in the numbers of the repeating unit. This property can be used to identify the natural variation found in every person's DNA since every person will have a different combination of STRs of different repeat length.

2. (a) Gel electrophoresis: Used to separate the DNA fragments (STRs) according to size to create the fingerprint or profile.
(b) PCR: Used to make many copies of the STRs. Only the STR sites are amplified by PCR, because the primers used to initiate the PCR are very specific.

3. (a) Extract the DNA from sample. Treat the tissue with chemicals and enzymes to extract the DNA, which is then separated and purified.
(b) Amplify the microsatellite using PCR. Primers are used to make large quantities of the STR.
(c) Run the fragments through a gel to separate them.

The resulting pattern represents the STR sizes for that individual (different from that of other people).

4. To ensure that the number of STR sites, when compared, will produce a profile that is effectively unique (different from just about every other individual). It provides a high degree of statistical confidence when a match occurs.

174. Forensic Applications of DNA Profiling (page 231)
1. Profiles of everyone involved must be completed to compare their DNA to any DNA found at the scene and therefore eliminate (or implicate) them as suspects.

2. The alleged offender is not guilty. The alleged offender's DNA profile does not appear in the DNA collected at the crime scene nor does it appear in the DNA database. Profile E's DNA is found at the scene.

3. (a) 0.0294
(b) 0.3446
(c) $2pq = 2 \times 0.0294 \times 0.3446 = 0.0203$

4. 14-10, 14-11, 15-10, 15-11

5. (a) No
(b) The man cannot be the biological father because there are two mismatches in the profiles. The child does not show any matches with STR D19S433 and D2S441.

6. (a) Each whale species has a distinct DNA profile. Profiling the whale meat therefore reveals the types of whales they meat came from.
(b) Individual whales also have their own DNA profile. Profiling the whale meat from each species reveals how many whales of that species were killed (by simply counting the number of different profiles.

175. Hunting for a Gene (page 233)
1. The physical effects of Huntington's disease are shaking of hands and/or limbs and an awkward gait. More severe effects include the loss of muscle control and mental function leading to dementia.

2. The mHTT gene was discovered using information from the family history of 10,000 people. Using a probe called G8, a map of the 4th chromosome was built up and each gene sequenced. The mHTT gene was shown to be one with a trinucleotide repeat expansion.

3. HD is caused by a trinucleotide repeat expansion of the sequence CAG on the 4th chromosome. Repeats of over 35 cause the disease and the greater the number of repeats the more severe the disease. Because of the instability of the mHTT gene the number of repeats and severity of the disease tends to increase over generations.

176. Profiling for Analysis of Disease Risk (page 234)
1. (a) Haplotypes are used because the many SNPs in them fall into distinct combinations that can be matched statistically to a particular condition. Single SNPs will not provide enough information; there would be no way to match a particular SNP to a particular condition.
(b) In most cases, there will be people with the disease and people without the disease who have the same SNP or haplotype profile. Therefore the haplotype only gives a probability of a person having the disease.

2. Genomic analyses can provide probabilities for successful treatment outcomes, i.e. for a given genetic profile, a particular treatment will have a certain probability of being successful. This helps match drugs to a person's personal genetic profile based on their sequence variations.

177. Making Recombinant DNA (page 235)
1. Restriction enzymes cut DNA into lengths or to isolate genes by cutting at specific recognition sites.

2. Sticky ends on DNA allow different DNA strands cut with the same restriction enzyme to be joined (via the complementary overhanging base pairs. Blunt ends on DNA strands allow DNA strands of any other blunt end fragments to be joined.

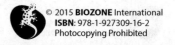
© 2015 **BIOZONE** International
ISBN: 978-1-927309-16-2
Photocopying Prohibited

The strands do not have to be complementary.

3. Having many different kinds of restriction enzymes allows DNA to be cut at many different recognition sites and so produce a variety of sticky or blunt ends. This allows for a better ability to isolate and join different regions of the DNA.

4. (a) The two single-stranded DNA molecules are recombined into a double-stranded molecule. This is achieved by H-bonding between complementary bases.
   (b) DNA ligase joins two adjacent pieces of DNA by linking nucleotides in the sticky ends.

5. It joins together DNA molecules, while restriction digestion (by restriction enzymes) cuts them up.

6. With a few exceptions, all organisms on Earth use the same DNA code to store information and the same cellular machinery to read the information and express it. Any DNA from any organism can therefore be read and expressed by the cellular machinery of any other organism into which the DNA is spliced.

178. The Applications of Transgenesis (page 237)
1. Transgenesis is the insertion of DNA from one species of organism into another.

2. Applications of transgenesis include (one of):
   – Modification of crop plants to alter their nutritional profile, environmental tolerance, or resistance to disease, pests, or herbicides.
   – Producing animals with specific genetic defects for medical or veterinary research so that disease processes can be studied and effective treatments can be developed.
   – Livestock improvement for characteristics such as wool or meat quality and quantity, and milk yield and nutritional profile.
   – Animal biofactories including the production of livestock that secrete therapeutic proteins in milk, or bacteria that produce valuable human proteins such as human insulin and factor VIII.

179. Vectors for Transgenesis (page 238)
1. (a) Viruses are good vectors because they are adapted to gain entry into a host's cells and integrate their DNA into that of the host.
   (b) Viral vectors can cause problems because (two of):
   • The host can develop a strong immune response to the viral infection. In patients disadvantaged (immune suppressed) by their disorder, this could severely undermine their health.
   • Viruses may not survive if attacked by the host's immune system.
   • Only short sequence of DNA can be carried by the virus.
   • The genes may integrate randomly into chromosomes and disrupt the functioning of normal genes.

2. Plasmids are used for:
   • Producing recombinant DNA for production of transgenic bacteria (or subsequent insertion into plants to produce genetically modified plant material).
   • Carrying new DNA into a cell for gene therapy.

180 Transgenic Plant: Golden Rice (page 239)
1. The genes for two different enzymes involved in beta carotene synthesis are taken from two different sources and inserted into the nuclear genome of a rice plant. Expression of the gene under the control of an endosperm specific promoter results in production of beta carotene in the edible portion of the rice plant.

2. The expression of the genes is controlled by a promoter specific to the endosperm, so the genes will only be expressed in that tissue.

3. *Agrobacterium tumefaciens* is a natural plant pathogen and can transfer genes as a consequence of infecting a host plant. The tumour-inducing *Ti* plasmid can be modified to delete the tumour-forming gene and insert a gene for a desirable trait.

4. (a) Production and consumption of beta-carotene rich rice could alleviate or prevent diseases related to vitamin A deficiency (e.g. night blindness and susceptibility to infection as a result of low immunity). Beta carotene is a precursor to vitamin A.
   (b) Improved nutrition through GM rice will be viable only if the diet in targeted regions is also adequate with respect to fat intake. In some impoverished regions this will not be the case, as diet is inadequate across a wide range of food groups, including fat and protein.

5. (a) More grains per head, larger grains.
   (b) Faster maturation time, even in marginal conditions.
   (c) Production of natural toxins, thicker seed cat, low palatability to insects, shift in timing of vulnerable stage.

181. Food for the Masses (page 241)
1. The bacterium because it uses only one enzyme to facilitate multiple reactions. It is therefore simpler to use in the production of the modified plant.

2. The gene can be isolated by first identifying the associated enzyme and its amino acid sequence. From this, the mRNA sequence can be identified. The correct mRNA molecules can then be extracted and reverse transcriptase used to copy the mRNA into DNA. This can then be amplified.

   Or - Once the DNA sequence is identified, PCR primers can be produced that will anneal to the start sequences of the gene. The PCR product will be the targeted gene.

   Or - The gene can be identified from its protein product (as above). This can then be cut from the chromosome using restriction enzymes and amplified.

3. *Agrobacterium*. This bacterium can transfer DNA into plants, so that the cells will contain recombinant DNA.

4. A plasmid (the *Ti* plasmid) is removed from the *Agrobacterium*. Using restriction enzymes the plasmid is cut and the target DNA inserted (the tumor forming gene is removed). DNA ligase is used to attach the target DNA to the plasmid. The plasmid is then replaced into the *Agrobacterium*.

5. (a) *Agrobacterium* transfers the recombinant plasmid to the cells of the target plant.
   (b) The best stage for transformation is while the plant is in embryonic form. In this way a larger proportion of the plant cells will be affected and take up the new DNA. This will cause a much better result in the adult plant.

6. Transformed plants can be identified if an extra gene is inserted along with the target gene. This is normally a gene for drug resistance. Plants grown on agar impregnated with the chemical will grow only if they have taken up the new DNA. Those without won't grow.

7. A large number of plants can be produced using vegetative propagation. In this way many plants can be produced, which will lead to rapid dissemination of the transgenic stock.

182. The Ethics of GMO Technology (page 243)
1. (a) Advantage: Crop growers would not need to spray for crops pest as often.
   (b) Problem: Plants producing toxins as a pest resistance may cause health problems if eaten over a long period of time. Pest resistant plants could become a problem outside the crop field (as weeds).

2. (a) Plants and animals could be used to produce commercial quantities of pharmaceuticals at an affordable cost for medicinal or industrial use.
   (b) Concerns over animal welfare and the long term effects of genetic modification on the animals and plants.

3. (a) Using transgenic livestock to improve yield or quality of product such as wool or meat.
   (b) Use of livestock as biofactories by producing useful proteins, such as anti-thrombin and alpha 1 antitrypsin, in their milk (cattle, sheep, and goats).
   (c) Because the cost of developing the technology is high, companies may recoup costs by applying for patents on the modified organisms so that they can control distribution and price. This increases costs to farmers (and to consumers).

© 2015 **BIOZONE** International
ISBN: 978-1-927309-16-2
Photocopying Prohibited

4. The widespread use of antibiotic marker genes in food crops for human consumption or stock food may give rise to antibiotic resistant strains of pathogenic bacteria which affect humans and stock animals. Restrained use of antibiotics is now considered essential in preventing large scale development of antibiotic resistance.

5. (a) Introduces nitrogen fixing ability in non-legumes thereby reducing the need for nitrogen fertilisers.
    (b) The bacterium would prevent attack on the seeds by pathogenic bacteria and fungi.

6. Note: This question was not intended to imply that ethical or moral concerns are any less real or valid than biological ones. It is an exercise in identifying biological concerns.

    (a) Some points for discussion are:
    –   The GM product or the GMO could have an undesirable effect on humans or other organisms.
    –   That the genetic modification would spread uncontrollably into other organisms (breeding populations of the same or different species).
    –   Consumer choice is denied unless adequate labelling protocols are in place. If everything contains GM products, there is no consumer choice.
    –   General fear of what is not understood (fear of real or imagined consequences).
    –   Objections on the grounds that it is ethically and morally wrong to tamper with the genetic make-up of an organism.
    –   Generation of monopolies where large companies control the rights to seed supplies & breeding stock.
    (b) Those that pose a real biological threat are:
    –   The indiscriminate spread of foreign genes (plants).
    –   Unusual reactions, e.g. allergies, to novel proteins.
    –   Some animal rights issues may be justified if genetic modification causes impaired health.

183. Gene Therapy (page 245)

1. (a) To correct a genetic disorder of metabolism by correction, replacement, or supplementation of a faulty gene with a corrected version.
    (b) Gene therapy might be used for inherited genetic disorders of metabolism, non-infectious acquired diseases (e.g. cancer), and infectious diseases.

2. Transfection of germline cells allows the genetic changes to be inherited. This means a heritable disorder can be corrected so that future generations will not carry the fault. Transfection of somatic cells only corrects those cells for their lifetime.

3. Gene amplification is used to make multiple copies of the normal (corrective) allele.

184. Using Gene Therapy to Treat Disease (page 246)

1. (a) CF symptoms include disruption of the function of secretory glands including the pancreas, intestinal glands, biliary tree, sweat glands, and bronchial glands. Infertility. Disruption of lung function caused by an accumulation of thick, sticky mucus in the lungs.
    (b) CF has been targeted because the majority of cases are the result of a gene defect involving the loss of only one triplet (three nucleotides). In theory, correction of this one gene should not be difficult.
    (c) Correction rate has been low (25%), and the effects of correction have been short lived and the benefits quickly reversed. These problems are related to the poor survival of the viral vector in the body and the sporadic functioning of the gene because it is not integrated into the host's (human) chromosome. Patients suffer problems with immune reaction to the vector. In one patient, treatment was fatal.

2. (a) **Vector**: Adenoviruses.
    Potential problems (not required): Poor integration and survival of vector. Immune reactions. Low corrective rates.
    (b) **Vector**: Liposomes
    Potential problems (not required): Liposomes are less efficient than viruses at transferring genes, so corrective rates are lower than for viral vectors.

3. (a) X-linked SCID is caused by a mutation to a gene on the X

chromosome that encodes for the common gamma chain. ADA SCID is caused by a defective gene that codes for adenosine deaminase.
    (b) The vector used in the treatment of SCID is a gutted retrovirus (a retrovirus with its natural genetic material removed to make room for the corrective gene being transferred).

4. Gene therapy for cystic fibrosis is targeted at the lungs using either an adenovirus or a liposome delivered via the airways. SCID is treated using a retrovirus, which is introduced to the patient's own bone marrow stem cells. These are then cultured and returned to the patient.

5. (a) Chance of interfering with essential gene function: When an essential gene function is affected by gene therapy in somatic cells, the individual will be affected. There may be a chance of corrective therapy in that person's lifetime. When the change affects germline cells, all descendants of the treated individual have a chance to inherit the disrupted gene, so a second heritable defect is created.
    (b) Misuse of the therapy to selectively alter phenotype: Alteration of somatic cells to selectively alter one's phenotype is (presumably) a matter of one's own choice; it may benefit that person in their own lifetime, but will not affect subsequent generations. When these selective changes affect the germline cells, then they are heritable and the alteration is not necessarily limited to one individual. This poses the problem of genetic selection and eugenics, and all their consequent ethical dilemmas.

185. Chapter Review (page 248)
No model answer. Summary is the student's own.

186. KEY TERMS: Did You Get It? (page 249)

1. annealing (B), DNA amplification (J), DNA ligation (L), DNA polymerase (O), gel electrophoresis (I), GMO (N), marker gene (G), microsatellite (M), PCR (H), primer (D), recognition site (F), recombinant DNA (K), restriction enzyme (E), sticky end (C), vector (A)

2. (a) C is the father.
    (b) These two individuals are homozygous for one allele therefore for that allele one band shows instead of two.

187. Natural Clones in Plants (page 251)

1. Vegetative propagation refers to the asexual means by which plants reproduce themselves. Natural means include rhizomes, tubers and runners. Artificial means include grafting and cuttings.

2. Enables the plant to have an overwintering food store from which it can mobilise food early on in the next growing season. This gives the plant a head start on plants that rely only on photosynthesis (light levels are often low early in the growing season).

3. Vegetative propagation has enabled the production of large numbers of plants from one successful (e.g. high yielding) variety. Successful combinations of genetic characteristics can be retained through vegetative propagation.

4. Vegetative reproduction enables a well adapted plant to spread rapidly and saturate its environment, out-competing plants that must wait to produce seeds.

5. (a) Vegetative propagation is a useful conservation strategy because it enables large numbers of plants to be produced without having to wait for them to set seed and reproduce sexually.
    (b) If plants are rare, vegetative propagation can boost numbers so that the population is less at risk of loss. When less at risk, sexual propagation (pollination and fertilisation) methods can be included.
    (c) Species reliant on vegetative propagation may lack the genetic diversity to remain viable. Genetic diversity is an important part of being able to produce adaptive phenotypes in case of environmental change.

© 2015 **BIOZONE** International
ISBN: 978-1-927309-16-2

6. A cutting is a portion of the parent plant that is removed and induced to grow into a new individual. Cuttings are used when one wants to merely propagate the features of the plant from which the cutting was taken. Grafting is a more complicated procedure where a scion from one individual is joined to the shoot of another plant (the rootstock). Grafting is used to incorporate the (favourable) features of two individual plants and produce a superior variety.

188. Micropropagation of Plant Tissue (page 253)

1. The purpose of micropropagation is to produce large numbers of clones (with identical phenotypic and genetic traits as the parent) in a short space of time.

2. Micropropagation can be used to increase the populations of rare plants or to rapidly increase the numbers of a commercially important plant variety or genetic line. It also overcomes the need for germination of seeds and so makes it quicker to produce large numbers of plants that take a long time to grow or reproduce naturally.

3. (a) A callus is a mass of undifferentiated cells.
    (b) Several plant hormones are added to the culture in sequence. These will stimulate each phase of plant development.

4. There is a much reduced gene pool because all the plants are effectively clones. The low genetic diversity reduces the ability of the population to adapt to changing environments. Many generations will be needed before any real genetic variation is restored through natural mutation of genes. The limited gene pool may also cause problems with fertility and seed germination and increases vulnerability to disease.

189. Natural Clones in Animals (page 255)

1. (a) Clones can arise through fragmentation (fragments of the animal grow into new individuals), by budding (offspring bud off the parent body), or by twinning (the splitting of a very early stage zygote).
    (b) Asexual reproduction produces clones because the new animal arises from genetic material identical to the parent, there is no combining with new genetic material or reshuffling of genes.

2. (a) Identical twins arise when a fertilised egg (zygote) divides into two separate embryos that then develop individually.
    (b) Identical twins are genetically identical to each other but not to the parents. Other natural clones are genetically identical to the parents.

190. Cloning by Embryo Splitting (page 256)

1. In embryo splitting, the zygote is split after the first division and the two cells are artificially separated and then allowed to proceed with their development. This is what happens naturally when identical twins are produced.

2. Embryo splitting allows breeders to produce multiple embryos that can be implanted into multiple surrogate mothers, producing multiple offspring.

3. Cloning high milk yielding cows will reduce the time it takes to produce a high producing herd. Multiple offspring will be produced quickly from the most valuable phenotypes. The genetic gain will be more rapid than that achieved by traditional selective breeding methods.

4. Repeated exclusive use of embryo splitting will reduce the total pool of genetic diversity from which to select new breeds/strains/varieties.

191. Cloning by Somatic Cell Nuclear Transfer (page 257)

1. (a) SCNT is the transfer of the nucleus of a somatic (body) cell into an egg cell which has had its nucleus removed. The hybrid cell can then be grown to produce a new (cloned) organism.
    (b) Embryo splitting produces twins that are genetically identical to each other but not to the parent or any other

animal. SCNT produces an animal that is genetically identical to the one that donated the somatic cell.

2. (a) Switching off genes in the donor cell: Induced by low nutrient medium.
    (b) Fusion of donor and enucleated egg: Induced by a short electric pulse.
    (c) Activation of the cloned cell: Induced by a second gentle electric pulse or by chemical means. A time delay of about 6 hours improves the success of the egg activation process, probably through the prolonged contact of the chromatin with (unknown) cytoplasmic factors.

3. Potential advantages:
    – Conservation of rare breeds. It is hoped that cloning will be integrated into zoo management programmes. By retaining the tissues of individuals before they die, some of the genetic diversity of rare species can be retained. It may even be possible to restore species that are on the verge of extinction using cloning technology.
    – Use in the development of treatments for genetic diseases.
    Potential disadvantages:
    – Efficiency of producing live clones is very low - the process is still technically difficult.
    – Ethical issues arise from the destruction of embryos.

192. The Use of Microbes in Food Technology (page 259)

1. Advantages include:
    – Cost effective production of a wide range of materials or foods.
    – Microbes can be grown on a wide range of materials, including waste products of other industrial processes.
    – Microbe growth takes up little space and processes can often be run continuously, with product being continuously removed.
    – Microbes can be used in the production and preservation of foodstuffs (e.g. cheese).

2. Many examples are possible:
    – In the dairy industry, use of GE rennin (chymosin) has improved the supply and quality control of this product. Use of GE bacteria has provided strains with particular properties and greater predictability.
    – In the beer and wine industry, use of GE yeasts has improved the efficiency of alcoholic production and produced strains with greater tolerance to high ethanol concentrations.

3. Fermentation lowers the pH of the cabbage and helps to stop food spoilage bacteria from growing.

193. Beer Brewing (page 260)

1. Sugar (glucose) → ethanol + carbon dioxide

2. (a) Malting: Barley seeds are steeped in water for one to two days and then spread out in a warm, damp place and left for a further 2-6 days to germinate. Gibberellic acid is sprayed on to aid germination. The germinated barley seed is called the malt. During germination, the amylase enzymes are mobilised. These are required to hydrolyze the starch (not usable by yeasts) to fermentable sugars.
    (b) Kilning: The malt is slowly dried by gradually heating to between 65° and 80°C. This kills the embryos without destroying the amylases. The higher the kilning temperature, the darker the beer.
    (c) Milling: The dried barley seeds are crushed to a coarse powder, called grist.
    (d) Mashing: The grist is steeped in warm water and the resulting mash is kept at 65°C for an hour to allow the amylases to break down the starch to fermentable sugars. Mashing also allows the sugars, amino acids, and mineral salts to diffuse from the seeds into the surrounding liquid. These nutrients are required for growth of the yeast.
    (e) Boiling: After mashing, the nutrient-rich liquor (wort) is separated from the residue by filtration and then boiled

(with hops). Boiling extracts the flavour compounds, stops further enzyme action, and precipitates out the tannins, proteins, phosphates that would otherwise make the beer cloudy.

(f) Fermentation: The boiled wort is cooled to 30°C and inoculated with yeast. It is left to ferment for 7-10 days, during which time the yeast degrades the sugars anaerobically and produces alcohol (ethanol) and carbon dioxide.

(g) Finishing: After fermentation, the beer is filtered to remove the yeast cells and any residue and impurities. A viscous solution called isinglass is used to flocculate the yeast for easier filtration. The brewer may recycle the yeast of use it elsewhere to make food products (e.g. yeast extracts). Traditional beers are stored in barrels and allowed to condition. Modern beer is pasteurised and standardised for taste, colour, etc. and then bottled or canned.

194. Bread Making (page 261)

1. (a) Sugar (sucrose): Food source for the yeast as is the flour (maltose).
   (b) Yeast: Ferments the dough by breaking down the sugar anaerobically to ethanol and carbon dioxide.
   (c) Water (or milk): Produces a thick, sticky dough (by the hydration of gluten, the proteins in the wheat flour) which is able to hold the leavening gases produced during the baking process.

2. (a) At the beginning of fermentation, enzymes in the yeast start breaking down starch into sugars. As the fermentation proceeds, the dough becomes more acidic. This is due in part to rising levels of carbon dioxide, but there are also more organic acids like ethanoic acid and lactic acid being formed from the ethanol in the dough. The acidity of the dough causes more molecules to break down and eventually the amount of ethanol formed starts to inhibit the yeast's activity.
   (b) Once the loaves have been molded into their final shape and deposited in baking pans, a second or final fermentation gives the dough once last chance to rise before baking.

3. Doughs made from gluten free flour (e.g. rye or barley) are less sticky and elastic, and are less capable of holding on to the leavening gases produced during the baking process. Thus the do not rise.

195. Cheese Making (page 262)

1. Annotated diagram should contain the following points:

   1. Pasteurisation of the milk at 72°C for 15 seconds.
   2. Starter culture added. Rennet added to coagulate milk
   3. Separation of curds and whey.
   4. Ripening and processing, including cooking, brining, and salting depending on the cheese being produced.

2. The ripening stage produces the different types of cheese. Aeration allows oxygen to reach the microorganism in the cheese, producing internal moulds that flavour the cheese and give it texture. Addition of gas producing bacteria (e.g. in Swiss cheese) produces cheeses with large holes.

3. (a) Pasteurisation kills any undesirable bacteria. Without it, the characteristics of the cheese could be altered or dangerous bacteria could grow in the milk or cheese.
   (b) 30ºC is the optimum temperature for the growth of the microbes used in cheese production.

4. The protein is denaturing due to drop in pH and it begins to produce an insoluble mass. Rennet also helps to destabilise the stable casein protein micelles, and the casein proteins precipitate out to form a gel.

5. The bacteria must be able to tolerate the high cooking temperatures. Non-thermophilic bacteria would die at these higher cooking temperatures.

196. Yoghurt Making (page 264)

1. The two starter bacteria each produce conditions which

encourage growth in the other species. Lactobacilli break down protein to release peptides, which encourage the growth of the streptococci. This in turn sees the streptococci produce methanoic acid which further stimulates lactobacilli growth. During the incubation period lactobaccilli also produces lactic acid and at the end of the incubation, the pH has fallen to around 4.4.

2. Both bacteria produce acids (streptococci produce methanoic acid and lactobaccilli lactic acid) thereby lowering the pH.

3. The bacteria are not harmful when ingested. (Many people feel that 'live' yoghurt is healthier and tastes better.)

4. Antibiotics would destroy the bacteria used in the starter culture.

197. Using Microbes to Make Food: Pros and Cons (page 265)

1. Advantages discussed should include:
   – Microorganisms can be grown on waste food products and so can be grown cheaply.
   – Growth of microbes in bioreactors allows for easy adjustment of conditions to ensure optimal growth.
   – Microbes can be genetically engineered to produce products once only obtainable from animals or plants. This makes production of these products (e.g. insulin) in commercial quantities easier and more cost efficient.
   – Microbes can be used to produce protein products similar to meat, removing barriers to obtaining proteins (e.g ethical reasons for vegetarians).

   Disadvantages could include:
   – Food made using microbes must be carefully prepared to strict standards to reduce chances of food poisoning.
   – There are still negative perceptions of microbes used to manufacture food, especially if those microbes are genetically modified.
   – Differences in enzymes produced by GM microbes can make the food manufacturing process more difficult (e.g. bitter cheeses produced using rennin from GE bacteria).

198. Penicillin Production (page 266)

1. Stirring distributes the nutrients and fungi evenly through the tank.

2. (a) The fungus respires aerobically and so needs air.
   (b) The tank could be contaminated and the batch ruined.

3. Penicillin is produced during the stationary phase of growth (slower growth rate). If too many nutrients are added, the fungus grows rapidly, but does not produce penicillin. Thus nutrients are added in small amounts.

4. There could be antibiotic in the waste product, which could be taken in by the animals eating it. The normal microbial flora of the gut would be exposed to the antibiotic and this may contribute to the spread of penicillin resistance in bacteria.

199. Insulin Production (page 267)

1. (a) Some problems include:
   – High cost (extraction from tissue is expensive).
   – Non-human insulin is different enough from human insulin to cause side effects.
   – The extraction methods did not produce pure insulin so the insulin was often contaminated.
   (b) Some advantages include:
   – Production can be continuous and is not limited by the availability of livestock.
   – Mass production of human proteins using *E. coli* facilitates a low cost, reliable supply for consumer use.
   – The insulin protein is free of contaminants and, because it is a human protein, the side effects of its use are minimised.

2. The insulin is synthesised as two (A and B) nucleotide sequences (corresponding to the two polypeptide chains) because a single sequence is too large to be inserted into the bacterial plasmid. Two shorter sequences are small enough to be inserted (separately) into bacterial plasmids.

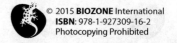

3. The β-galactosidase gene in *E.coli* has a promoter region so the synthetic genes must be tied to that gene in order to be transcribed.

4. (a) Insertion of the gene: The yeast plasmid is larger and can accommodate the entire synthetic nucleotide sequence for the A and B chains as one uninterrupted sequence. Only one chain can be manufactured by *E coli*. Different strains produce different chains (A or B).
   (b) Secretion and purification: Purification is simplified in yeast because removal of β-galactosidase is not required and the separate protein chains do not need to be joined (unlike insulin produced using *E. coli*).
   (c) Yeast. As a eukaryote *Saccharomyces* has secretory pathways that are more similar to humans than those of a prokaryote and the β-galactosidase promoter is not required so secretion of the precursor insulin molecules is less problematic.

200. Bioremediation (page 269)
1. Bioremediation is the use of living organisms to remove or neutralise pollutants in the environment.

2. Bacteria can be added either *in situ* or *ex situ*. *Ex situ* use of bacteria requires the contaminated soil be moved off site. Bacteria (e.g. those used in the product Oilzapper) are added. They metabolise the oil, increasing in number as they do so. For marine oil spills, bacteria may be introduced directly to oil while at sea. Dispersants help break up the oil into droplets making a greater surface area for the bacteria. The bacteria metabolise the oil into water and carbon dioxide.

3. Genetic engineering can be used to add genes that enhance the ability of the bacteria to metabolise oil or digest other contaminants, e.g. *Deinococcus radiodurans* digests ionic mercury from radioactive nuclear waste. Equally, genetic engineering is used to add genes that will stop the bacteria from spreading to useful oil supplies.

201. Techniques in Microbial Culture (page 270)
1. Aseptic technique ensures there is no contamination of the plate from other microbes in the environment.

2. The heat from the loop would kill any microbes it touched.

202. Strain Isolation (page 271)
1. Streak plating isolates individual colonies, making them easier to study and/or count.

2. Streak plating is based on the progressive reduction in the number of bacteria used to make each new streak. By the time the last streak is completed, the sample is so diluted that individual colonies may be isolated.

3. Petri dish lids are only partially removed to help prevent microbes in the air or on dust settling onto the agar and contaminating it.

4. Use selective media when there are two microbial types (strains or species) present, with the same colony morphology, and it is not possible to separate them visually.

203. Dilution Plating (page 272)
1. 19 colonies X 100 000 = 1.9×10^6 cells per cm^3

2. (a) Viable count: The number of living cells in the culture (cells capable of reproducing).
   (b) In dilution plating, only viable cells will give rise to countable colonies. The calculated culture density will therefore refer to the number of viable cells.
   (c) Turbidimetry: An indirect method where culture turbidity is measured using absorbance on a colorimeter. The colorimeter is set at zero using the culture medium and subsequent absorbance readings above zero are taken as measures of microbial density. The culture density is determined from a standard calibration curve (absorbances established for known densities of that culture type). The technique provides no indication of

viable cells, since most cells (except those that have sedimented out) will contribute to the absorbance reading.

204. Industrial Microbiology (page 273)
1. A continuous culture system provides a constant supply of fresh culture medium while removing product/spend culture at the same rate. In contrast, a batch culture adds cells to a fixed volume of medium and the process is halted when the appropriate stage of culture growth has been reached.

2. This keeps the cells actively growing and dividing (this is when they produce the product). It is undesirable for them to enter the stationary phase (which they would do if they exhausted the growth medium).

3. Batch culture is used when a secondary metabolite is being harvested.

4. Asepsis prevents the contamination of the culture with undesirable organisms which, if present, may compete with the desirable microbes and cause a change in the nature or quality of the end product, low product yield, and loss of time and profit.

5. (a) Heat can be dissipated by using a water jacket (containing cooling water). It is assisted by the physical mixing of the culture.
   (b) Oxygen demand is met by aerating the culture using a diffuser (sparger), a perforated disc which disperses air through the medium.
   (c) Nutrient levels are monitored throughout the culture process and demand is met by addition of new culture medium (or end-harvest) when indicated.

205. Microbial Growth and Metabolites (page 275)
1. (a) The initial lag is a result of there being little or no cell division occurring, hence no perceivable growth in cell number (the cells are increasing in size and synthesising enzymes, but not dividing).
   (b) The lag can be reduced by placing actively dividing cells into a new culture medium (i.e. starting the culture with actively dividing cells).

2. Adding fresh nutrients and removing toxic by-products keeps the culture in the maximal log phase of growth. This is especially important if the product being harvested is a primary metabolite.

3. Primary metabolite is a product that is formed at the same time as the cells (growth and production curves are similar). Secondary metabolites are produced after the microbe has largely completed its growth and has entered into the stationary phase.

4. (a) Because it is produced as a product of metabolism.
   (b) Secondary metabolites are not immediately essential for microbial survival but are produced at the end of the active growth phase, so the maximum yield occurs after growth slows.

5. Secondary metabolites are produced in response to depletion of nutrients or build-up of waste products, often as a defence or competitive strategy. They therefore are not produced until active growth has slowed.

206. Plotting Microbial Growth (page 277)
Erratum first printing of workbook: In the first sentence of the introductory paragraph remove the word mitotic. Binary fission is a simple cell division.... Apologies for any confusion caused.
1. Completed table below:

Min	No.	Min	No.	Min	No.
0	1	140	128	260	8 192
20	2	160	256	280	16 384
40	4	180	512	300	32 768
60	8	200	1024	320	65 536
80	16	220	2048	340	131 072
100	32	240	4096	360	262 144
120	64				

2. (a) 8   (b) 512   (c) 262 144

© 2015 **BIOZONE** International
ISBN: 978-1-927309-16-2
Photocopying Prohibited

3. and 4(b)

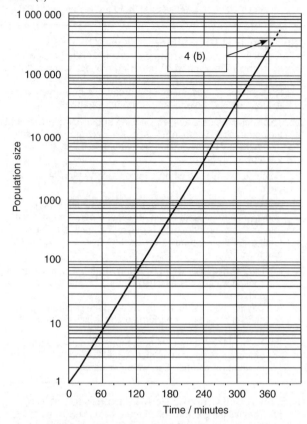

4. (a) 524 288
   (b) see graph above

5. Withe exponential growth, the numbers are very low initially, but increase quickly and very large numbers are involved. The log graph makes it feasible to plot the very small and very large numbers together in a reasonable space and in a way that is easy to read and interpret.

207. Immobilised Enzymes (page 278)
1. (a) Benefits of immobilised enzymes (any two):
   – Easy recovery of enzyme for reuse.
   – Easy harvesting of enzyme-free end-product.
   – Greater stability (protection of a solid matrix).
   – Continuous fermentation is possible
   – Keeps proteolytic enzymes apart so that they do not digest each other.
   – Lower cost (because enzymes can be reused).
   (b) Disadvantage of immobilised enzymes (any of):
   – Immobilisation may be difficult to achieve.
   – Immobilisation may lower enzyme activity and reaction rates.
   – Immobilisation technique may not be stable; enzymes may eventually wash away.

2. Any of the following:
   – Encapsulation may make it difficult for enzyme and substrate to interact.
   – Covalent bonding may damage the enzyme or subtly interfere with the active site.
   – Entrapment may affect charges on the enzyme and affect interaction with the substrate. The enzyme may also leak away.
   – Reaction rates may be slowed if rates of diffusion of substrate and end-product into and out of a matrix are reduced.
   – Adsorbed enzymes are not firmly attached and may wash away.

208. Immobilisation of Lactase (page 279)
1. Milk is a very good food source (it contains good levels of macronutrients, vitamins, and minerals). Being able to drink milk throughout life means all people could benefit from its nutritional value.

2. The enzyme lactase is immobilised to remove lactose from milk. It does so by binding the lactose and enzymatically hydrolysing it into glucose and galactose.

3. One of the products of lactose hydrolysis (glucose) is sweeter than lactose itself. Therefore, lactose free milk tastes sweeter than ordinary milk.

209. Applications of Enzymes (page 280)
1. Any one of:
   Aminoacyclase: Catalyses the degradation of an acyl amino acid in the presence of water into a carboxylic acid and an L-amino acid. Industrially, it is used to produce amino acids for the production of dietary supplements.

   Glucoamlyase: The major application of glucoamylase is the conversion of starch/dextrin to glucose, which is essential for numerous fermentation processes in a range of food and beverage industries.

   Nitrilase: Nitrilases including nitrile hydratase are used in the treatment of waste water and in the conversion of acrylonitrile to acrylamide. Nitrilases catalyse the general reaction $R-C=N + H_2O \rightarrow R-C(O)NH_2$ (converting nitriles to amides).

210. Industrial Production of Enzymes (page 281)
1. (a) In the production of intracellular enzymes, the microbial cells must first be separated from the culture medium and then disrupted. The production of extracellular enzymes does not require this cellular disruption.
   (b) Cellular disruption is required to release intracellular enzymes from within the cells. Extracellular enzymes are present in the medium after being secreted by the cells.

2. A crude extract is cheaper to produce. In some applications, a highly purified product is not required, so the crude product can be used.

211. Chapter Review (page 282)
No model answer. Summary is the student's own.

212. KEY TERMS: Did You Get It? (page 283)
1. aseptic technique (I), batch culture (P), bioreactor (K), bioremediation (A), biotechnology (J), clone (E), continuous culture (N), cutting (H), embryo splitting (O), enzyme immobilisation (C), lag phase (L), micropropagation (F), primary metabolite (D), secondary metabolite (B), somatic cell nuclear transfer (G), strain isolation (M)

2. Letter order (top to bottom): D, C, A, B

213. Components of an Ecosystem (page 285)
1. A community is a naturally occurring group of organisms living together as an ecological entity. The community is the biological part of the ecosystem. The ecosystem includes all of the organisms (the community) and their physical environment.

2. The biotic factors are the influences that result from the activities of living organisms in the community whereas the abiotic (physical) factors comprise the non-living part of the community, e.g. climate.

3. (a) Population   (c) The community
   (b) Ecosystem   (d) Physical factor

214. Types of Ecosystems (page 286)
1. (a) Yosemite National Park: ecosystem boundaries are the (artificial) boundaries of the park. It is part of the Sierra Nevada mountain range.
   (b) The clearing's border is the edge of the grass clearing

© 2015 **BIOZONE** International
ISBN: 978-1-927309-16-2
Photocopying Prohibited

where forest trees grow again.
(c) The tree ecosystem borders are the tree and soil and air immediately around it.

215. Ecosystems Are Dynamic (page 287)

1. A dynamic system is one that is constantly changing. Ecosystems, although they may appear constant are continually changing in response to changes in the weather and seasons and the activities of the organisms in them.

2. (a) Any two of: fire, flood, seasonal drought, landslides.
   (b) Open pit mining, large scale forest clearance, volcanic eruptions, inundation caused by sea level rise, prolonged drought (desert formation) as caused by climate shifts.

3. A climax community is one that apparently remains the same over time (there is no succession to a different community). However, an ecosystem is constantly changing. In a climax community, an equilibrium exists between growth and death in the community so that it appears static over the long term.

216. Food Chains (page 288)

1. (a) The sun.
   (b) The energy is converted to biomass through the process of photosynthesis.
   (c) Refer to the diagram, below

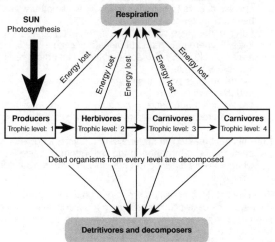

Some secondary consumers feed directly off decomposer organisms

2. Energy is transferred in the chemical bonds in biomass.

3. (a) Producers obtain energy from the sun via photosynthesis, the process by which the energy is converted to biomass.
   (b) Consumers obtain energy by eating other organisms.
   (c) Detritivores obtain energy from eating dead organic matter.
   (d) Saprotrophs obtain energy by extracellular digestion of dead material.

217. Food Webs (page 289)

1. (a) Carnivore   (d) Autotroph
   (b) Detritivore   (e) Herbivore (when young)
   (c) Detritus

2. Most energy is lost from the system as heat, so very little is transferred to the next level. After six links there is very little energy left in the system (not enough energy available to support the organisms in another level).

218. Constructing a Food Web (page 290)

1. Some food chain examples as below (there are others)
   (a) Algae → zooplankton → diving beetle
   (b) Algae → zooplankton → stickleback → pike
   (c) Macrophyte → great pond snail → herbivorous water beetle → stickleback → pike
   (d) Macrophyte → carp → pike
   (e) Algae → mosquito larva → *Hydra* → dragonfly larva →

carp → pike
   (f) Macrophyte → herbivorous water beetle → carp → pike
   (g) Algae → zooplankton → *Asplanchna* → leech → dragonfly larva → carp → pike
   (h) Detritus → *Paramecium* → A*splanchna* → leech → dragonfly larva → carp → pike
   (i) Detritus → great pond snail → leech → dragonfly larva → carp → pike
   (j) Detritus → *Paramecium* → mosquito larva → *Hydra* → dragonfly larva → carp→ pike

2.
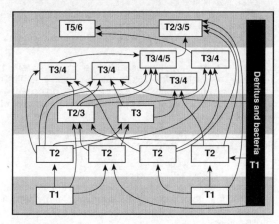

219. Energy Flow in an Ecosystem (page 292)

1. (a) 14 000   (b) 180
   (c) 35   (d) 100

2. Solar energy

3. A. Photosynthesis
   B. Eating/feeding/ingestion
   C. Respiration
   D. Export (lost from this ecosystem to another)
   E. Decomposers and detritivores feeding on other decomposers and detritivores
   F. Radiation of heat to the atmosphere
   G. Excretion/egestion/death

4. (a) 1 700 000 ÷ 7 000 000 x 100 = 24.28%
   (b) It is reflected. Plants appear green because those wavelengths are not absorbed. Reflected light falls on other objects as well as back into space.

5. (a) 87 400 ÷ 1 700 000 x 100 = 5.14%
   (b) 1 700 000 - 87 400 = 1 612 600 (94.86%)
   (c) Most of the energy absorbed by producers is not used in photosynthesis. This excess energy, which is not fixed, is lost as heat (although the heat loss component before the producer level is not usually shown on energy flow diagrams). Note: Some of the light energy absorbed through accessory pigments widens the spectrum that can drive photosynthesis. However, accessory pigment activity is mostly associated with absorbing and dissipating excess light energy that would damage chlorophyll.

6. (a) 78 835 kJ
   (b) 78 835 ÷ 1 700 000 x 100 = 4.64%

7. (a) Decomposers and detritivores
   (b) Transport by wind or water to another ecosystem (e.g. blown or carried in water currents).

8. (a) Low oxygen or anaerobic, low temperature, low moisture.
   (b) Energy remains locked up in biomass (not released).
   (c) Geological reservoir:

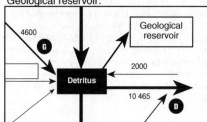

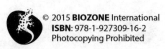
© 2015 **BIOZONE** International
ISBN: 978-1-927309-16-2
Photocopying Prohibited

(d) Oil (petroleum) and natural gas, formed from the remains of marine plankton. Coal and peat are both of plant origin; peat is partly decomposed, and coal is fossilised.

9. (a) 87 400 → 14,000:   14 000 ÷ 87 400 x 100 = 16%
   (b) 14 000 → 1600:   1600 ÷14 000 x 100 = 11.4%
   (c) 1600 → 90:   90 ÷ 1600 x 100 = 5.6

---

220. Ecological Pyramids (page 294)

1. (a) Number pyramid: Numbers of individual organisms at each trophic level.
   (b) Biomass pyramid: Weight (usually dry weight) of all organisms at each trophic level.
   (c) Energy pyramid: Energy content of all organisms at each trophic level.

2. Biomass or energy pyramids usually more accurately reflect the energy available to the next trophic level than pyramids of numbers. Pyramids of numbers can be misleading because a small number of producers may represent a large amount of biomass or energy.

3. Producers include the large trees. These have a large biomass and energy content per individual.

4. (a) 8690 → 142 = 8548 kJ = 1.6%
   (b) 142 → 12 = 130 kJ = 8.5%
   (c) Energy passed on from producers to primary consumers is less than the expected 10% because a lot of energy is diverted to the decomposers.
   (d) Decomposers.
   (e) In a plankton community, turnover times (the generation times of organisms) are very short and there is a lot of dead material in the water column and on the bottom. This provides a rich energy source to support a large decomposer biomass.

5. The algae are reproducing at a rapid rate, but are being heavily cropped by the larger zooplankton biomass.

---

221. Production and Trophic Efficiency (page 296)
or the producer biomass produced per area per unit time.

1. (a)- (c) and any of the following:
   - Amount and availability of light for photosynthesis. This is higher in the tropics.
   - Temperature. Higher temperatures are generally conducive to higher productivity.
   - Availability of water. Photosynthesis (and therefore productivity) will be limited when water is scarce.
   - Availability of nutrients. Nutrient limitations will limit plant growth and lower productivity.

2. (a)-(b) any of the following:
   - High diversity of grassland species contributing to ecosystem efficiencies (different tolerances and preferences so photosynthesis is maximised).
   - High root production typical of herbaceous species.
   - High producer turnover because continual cropping by herbivores keeps plants actively growing.
   - High rates of nutrient recycling so nutrient availability is not a factor in limiting productivity.
   - Savanna occurs in equatorial or near equatorial latitudes so high light and temperature help to increase rates of plant photosynthesis.
   - Continual supplies of nutrient from the dung of primary consumers (grazing herbivores).

3. (a) The key factors limiting rates of primary production in **terrestrial** ecosystems are temperature and moisture; the productivity of tundra ecosystems is limited by low temperatures, while that of desert ecosystems is limited by moisture availability. Tropical rainforest ecosystems do not have these same limitations.
   (b) In aquatic systems, light and nutrient availability limit rates of production. The NPP of open ocean is low relative to coastal systems because of the low levels of nutrients. Nitrogen and phosphorus, in particular, are very low in the open ocean but higher in coastal systems which receive inputs from the land.

Note: Although light may be limiting to productivity in the open ocean, tropical waters are less productive than one would predict from the higher light intensities there; low nutrient availability is the critical factor in this case.

4. (a) NPP of a particular crop can be maximised by reducing losses to pests, spraying to reduce losses to disease, maximising light penetration and nutrient uptake by keeping competing plants to a minimum, ensuring adequate amounts of water and nutrients.
   (b) Livestock productivities can be maximised using the same principles: minimising levels of disease and ensuring optimum nutrition, optimising stocking densities to reduce stress, reducing energy losses by restricting excessive movement (smaller paddocks) and providing shelter belts or indoor housing in colder weather.

5. Deserts are often high light environments, but are limited by water and nutrient availability so productivities are low. Intensive horticultural land is provided with plentiful water and nutrients and crops are often kept in climate controlled environments to maximise temperatures and raise carbon dioxide levels. The result is very high productivities (maintained by continual high inputs of energy and matter).

---

222. Nutrient Cycles (page 298)

1. (a) Bacteria are able to make conversions to and from elements and their ionic states. This gives plants and animals access to nutrients that they would otherwise not have (i.e. increases bioavailability).
   (b) Fungi decompose organic matter, returning nutrients to the soil where plants and bacteria can access them. They are also able to convert some nutrients into more readily accessible forms.
   (c) Plants are able make their own food and, when they die, add this to the soil in the form of nutrients that can be broken down and used by bacteria and fungi. They also provide browsing animals with nutrients when they are eaten.
   (d) Animals break down materials from plants, fungi and bacteria and return then to the soil with their wastes and when they die allowing the nutrients in them to re-enter the cycle.

2. The rates of decomposition are very high in the higher temperatures of tropical forests. As a result, decaying matter is processed very quickly and very little remains in the soil. Much of the carbon and other nutrients are also locked up in biomass.

3. A macronutrient is one that is required in large amounts. Micronutrients (also called trace elements) are needed in much smaller amounts.

---

223. The Nitrogen Cycle (page 299)

1. (a)-(e) any of:
   - Decomposition or decay of dead organisms, to ammonia by decomposer bacteria (ammonification).
   - Nitrification of ammonium ions to nitrite by nitrifying bacteria such as *Nitrosomonas* ($NH_4^+ \rightarrow NO_2^-$)
   - Nitrification of nitrite to nitrate by nitrifying bacteria such as *Nitrobacter* ($NO_2^- \rightarrow NO_3^-$)
   - Denitrification of nitrate to nitrogen gas by anaerobic denitrifying bacteria such as *Pseudomonas* ($NO_3^- \rightarrow N_{2(g)}$)
   - Fixation of atmospheric nitrogen to nitrate by nitrogen fixing bacteria such as *Azotobacter* and *Rhizobium* ($N_2 \rightarrow NO_3^-$)
   - Fixation of atmospheric nitrogen to ammonia by nitrogen fixing cyanobacteria ($N_2 \rightarrow NH_3$)

2. (a) Oxidation of atmospheric nitrogen by lightning.
   (b) Nitrogen fixation (by bacteria).
   (c) Production of nitrogen fertiliser by the Haber process

3. Denitrification.

4. The atmosphere.

5. Nitrate.

6. Any one of: Amino acids, proteins, chlorophyll.

7. Animals obtain their nitrogen by ingesting (eating) food (plants or other animals).

8. Leguminous material is high in nitrogen. Ploughing it in replenishes soil nitrogen and reduces the need for additional nitrogen fertiliser when growing non-leguminous crops subsequently.

9. (a)-(e) any five in any order:
   – Addition of nitrogen fertilisers to the land. This supplies inorganic nitrogen, as nitrate, for plant growth, but excess nitrogen, not absorbed by plants, may enter and pollute water sources.
   – Industrial physical-chemical fixation of nitrogen (through the Haber process) combines H and N to ammonia, which can be used to manufacture inorganic nitrogen fertilisers. This is an industrial process, requiring high temperatures and pressures and a large amount of energy. The effects of applied inorganic nitrogen are outlined above.
   – Genetic modification of plants so that they can fix nitrogen. The effect of this is to increase the range of crop plants capable of growing on nitrogen deficient soils. Potentially, this could make a beneficial contribution to soil fertility.
   – Large-scale, assisted composting produces nitrogen rich organic fertiliser which has the effect of improving soil fertility and structure. This has beneficial effects in reducing the amount of inorganic nitrogen fertiliser that must be applied for the desired plant growth.
   – Burning and harvesting removes nitrogen from the land and releases nitrogen oxides into the air.
   – Discharge of effluent (particular animal waste) into waterways enriches water bodies and leads to localised pollution and eutrophication.
   – Irrigation can accelerate loss of nitrate from the soil by increasing the rate at which nitrates are washed out of the soil into ground water.

224. The Carbon Cycle (page 301)

1. Arrows can be added for the points (a)-(d) as follows:
   (a) Dissolving of limestone by acid rain: Arrow from the limestone layer to atmospheric CO_2.
   (b) Release of carbon from the marine food chain: Arrows (labelled **respiration**) from marine organisms (shark, algae, fish) to atmospheric CO_2.
   (c) Mining and burning of coal: Arrow from the coal seam to atmospheric CO_2.
   (d) Burning of plant material: Arrow (labelled **combustion**) from the trees and/or grassland to atmospheric CO_2.

2. (a) **Respiration** (stepwise oxidation of glucose) and **combustion** (rapid oxidation of organic substances).
   (b) Both involve the release of CO_2.

3. (a) - (d) in any order:
   Atmosphere; coal; limestone; oil and natural gas.

4. (a) Photosynthesis   (b) Respiration

5. Carbon would eventually be locked up in the bodies (remains) of dead organisms. Dead matter would not rot. Possible gradual loss of CO_2 from the atmosphere.

6. (a) Coal: Plant material trapped under sediment in swampy conditions millions of years ago.
   (b) Oil: Marine plankton rapidly buried in sediment mya.
   (c) Limestone (also chalk = fine limestone): Shells of molluscs, skeletons of coral and other marine organisms with skeletons of calcium carbonate piled upon seabeds and compressed.
   (d) Peat: Partly decayed vegetation formed because of acidic or anaerobic conditions.

7. Plants and other producers use carbon dioxide as the raw material to produce carbon-containing compounds via photosynthesis. Consumers utilise these carbon based compounds as food and incorporate that carbon into their own tissues. During respiration, all organisms transfer the energy in organic compounds to ATP and release carbon dioxide into the atmosphere. When organisms die, decomposition of their tissues returns carbon to the carbon pool. The carbon that is not utilised by decomposers may be incorporated into fossil fuels or other carbon sinks.

8. (a) Humans deplete the carbon stored in sinks through extraction and combustion of fossil fuels.
   (b) Human activity has resulted in an increase in atmospheric levels of carbon dioxide.

225. Measuring Carbon Fluxes (page 303)

1. See graph at the top of the next page.

2. (a) Atmospheric carbon decreases.
   (b) i. Biospheric carbon increases
       ii. CO_2 from the atmosphere is fixed as organic carbon which can be stored in wood, or buried, eventually forming peat or coal.

3. Increased cellular respiration increases atmospheric carbon and decreases biospheric carbon.

4. (a) Deforestation, combustion of fossil fuels.
   (b) Atmospheric carbon dioxide holds heat, causing the global climate to warm.

226. Primary Succession (page 305)

1. Glacial retreat, exposed slip, new volcanic island.

2. (a) Lichens, mosses, liverworts, and hardy annual herb species are often the first to colonise bare ground.
   (b) (i) Chemically and physically erode rock (producing the beginnings of a soil). (ii) Add nutrients by decay.

3. Climax communities tend to have higher biodiversity and a more complex trophic structure than early successional communities. A greater diversity of community interactions buffers the system against disturbances because there are many more organisms with different ecological roles able to compensate for losses from the system.

227. Succession on Surtsey Island (page 306)

1. Surtsey was ideal as a study site for primary succession because it was an entirely new island, devoid of any soil, and was isolated from nearby influences (such as already established vegetation or urban settlements) that could accelerate the succession process.

2. Early colonisations were the result of seeds blown from Iceland to the Northern shore, which is the closest shore. Later colonisations were in the south due to the establishment of the gull colony. The gulls would transport seeds and contribute to soil fertility.

3. (a) 1985.
   (b) Transported by birds.
   (c) 1985. This coincides with the establishment of the gull colony as the gulls were instrumental in dispersing seeds.

228. Deflected Succession (page 307)

1. A deflected succession is a maintained climax community that is different to the one that would have appeared if no disturbances (and continued disturbance) had occurred.

2. If left to develop naturally, the biodiversity of an ecosystem changes. Animals and plants living there are out-competed and are lost from that area. To maintain their presence some areas are artificially maintained. For example moorlands are periodically mowed or burned to maintain the heather, Brauton Burrows is managed to maintain its dune community.

3. Where forest once prevailed, there is now meadow and grassland. The grazing of sheep and cattle maintain the meadows by eating any tree seedlings that may establish.

229. Measuring Distribution and Abundance (page 308)

1. Distribution describes the location of individuals of a species in an area. Abundance is how many of a species there are.

2. (a) Quadrat sampling
   (b) Belt transect
   (c) Area sampling

3. Information about the physical environment can help explain the distribution and abundance of the species being sampled.

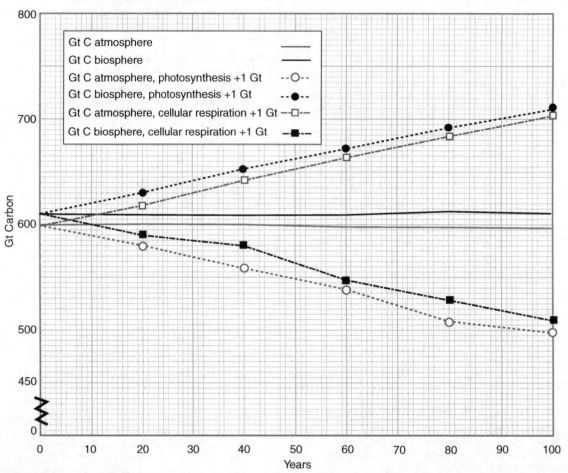

Effect of cellular respiration and photosynthesis on Gt atmospheric and biospheric carbon

230. Quadrat Sampling (page 309)

1. Mean number of centipedes captured per quadrat:
   Total number centipedes ÷ total number quadrats
   30 individuals ÷ 37 quadrats
   = 0.811 centipedes per quadrat

2. Number per quadrat ÷ area of each quadrat
   $0.811 ÷ 0.08 = 10.1$ centipedes per m^2

3. Clumped or random distribution.

4. Presence of suitable microhabitats for cover (e.g. logs, stones, leaf litter) may be scattered.

231. Quadrat-Based Estimates (page 310)

1. Species abundance in plant communities can be determined by using quadrats and transects, and abundance scales and percentage cover are often appropriate. Methods for sampling animal communities are more diverse, and density is a more common measure of abundance.

2. **Size**: Quadrat must be large enough to be representative and small enough to minimise the amount of sampling effort.

3. **Habitat heterogeneity**: Diverse habitats require more samples to be representative because they are not homogeneous.

4. (a) and (b) any two of:
   - The values assigned to species on the abundance scale are subjective and may not be consistent between users.
   - An abundance scale may miss rarer species and overestimate conspicuous ones.
   - The scale may be inappropriate for some habitats.
   - The semi-quantitative values assigned to the abundance categories cover a range so results will lack precision.

232. Sampling a Rocky Shore Community (page 311)

The results *per se* are not particularly important, but it is important to understand the method and its limitations. The results will vary depending on a group's agreed criteria for

inclusion of organisms in a given quadrat (e.g. when and how an organism is counted when it is partly inside a quadrat).
Note: Some algae are almost obscured by organisms or have other algae on top of them.

6. Typical results (total for each category) are:

	A	B	C	D	Direct count
Barnacle :	9	6	6	16	80
Oyster borer:	0	0	1	1	3
Chiton:	1	0	1	0	3
Limpet:	0	3	0	0	6
Algae:	27	18	15	13	101

7. Typical results for calculated population density based on A-D and on a direct count (question 8b):

	A	B	C	D	Direct count
Barnacle:	1667	1111	1111	2963	2469
Oyster borer:	0	0	185	185	93
Chiton:	185	0	185	0	93
Limpet:	0	556	0	0	185
Algae:	5000	3333	2778	2407	3117

NB: Area of 6 quadrats = $(0.03 × 0.03) × 6 = 0.0054\ m^2$
Area of total sample area = $0.18 × 0.18 = 0.0324\ m^2$

8. (a) Once the quadrats have been laid, the animals moving from one quadrat to another might be counted twice. The quadrat could involve the placement of physical barriers between each quadrat. There is a possibility of exposing the entire area and photographing it for later analysis.
   (b) Densities calculated on direct count in the last column of the table above. Students should be aware of the dangers of extrapolating data from a small sample. Including or excluding single individuals can have a large effect on the density calculated, particularly where species are present at low densities. Extension: Groups could combine data to

© 2015 **BIOZONE** International
ISBN: 978-1-927309-16-2
Photocopying Prohibited

see if they get a more representative sample (i.e. closer to the direct count).

233. Field Study of a Rocky Shore (page 313)
1. Hypothesis (c): The communities of intertidal animals differ between exposed rocky shores and sheltered rocky shores.

2. See table below

3. See graph below.

4. (a) The mean, medians, and modes are all similar.
   (b) The data are normally distributed.

5. (a) Rock oyster
   (b) Site A is open to the swell, which dislodges the oysters. Site B is more sheltered.

6. (a) Brown and plicate barnacles have a preference for exposed rocky shores.
   (b) Oyster borers are predators of brown and plicate barnacles so are more abundant when brown and plicate barnacles are also abundant.

6. (a) There are relatively high numbers of limpets at each site.
   (b) Limpets have a wide range of tolerance and are therefore able to live in many areas.

235. Chi-Squared Exercise in Ecology (page 317)
1. (a) H_0: "There is no difference between the numbers of periwinkles associated with different seaweed species".
   (b) H_A: "There is a real difference between the numbers of periwinkles associated with different seaweed species. Periwinkles show preference for the seaweed species with which they associate".

2. (a) Completed table:

Category	O	E	O – E	$(O-E)^2$	$\frac{(O-E)^2}{E}$
Spiral wrack	9	30	−21	441	14.70
Bladder wrack	28	30	−2	4	0.13
Toothed wrack	19	30	−11	121	4.03
Knotted wrack	64	30	34	1156	38.53
	Σ 120				Σ 57.4

(b) χ^2 = 57.39 (57.4)
(c) Degrees of freedom = 3 (4-1)
(d) The critical value of χ^2 at $P = 0.05$ and at d.f.= 3 is 7.82. The calculated χ^2 is (much) greater than the critical value (57.4 >> 7.82). *This means that* **by chance alone**, *a χ^2 value of 57.4 could be expected less than 0.1% of the time.*
(e) Reject H_0: The data are strongly in favour of H_A. Periwinkles show significant preference for one seaweed species (knotted wrack) over the others.

3. (a) H_0: "There is no difference between the number of woodlice in each habitat; woodlice show no preference for either habitat".
   H_A: "There is a real difference between the numbers of woodlice found in dry and humid conditions".
   (b) Calculation of χ^2:
   − Total no. of woodlice observed in dry = 15
   − Total no. of woodlice observed in humid = 35

Table: Total and mean numbers of intertidal animals at two rocky shore sites.

		Brown barnacle	Oyster borer	Columnar barnacle	Plicate barnacle	Rock oyster	Ornate limpet	Radiate limpet	Black nerite
Site A	Total number of animals	308	46	78	386	0	63	47	55
	Mean animals per m²	39	6	10	48	0	8	6	7
	Median value	38.5	6	9.5	51	0	7.5	6	7
	Modal value	-	7	8	-	-	-	6	-
Site B	Total number of animals	52	15	427	85	49	50	96	29
	Mean animals per m²	7	2	53	11	6	6	12	4
	Median value	7	2	56.5	10.5	7.5	6.5	12.5	3.5
	Modal value	7	-	58	-	8	5	14	-

Number of intertidal animals per m² of rocky shore

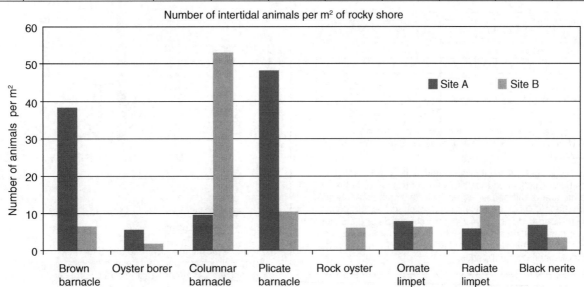

© 2015 **BIOZONE** International
ISBN: 978-1-927309-16-2
Photocopying Prohibited

Completed table:

Category	O	E	O – E	(O – E)^2	$\frac{(O – E)^2}{E}$
Dry atmosphere	15	25	–10	100	4
Humid atmosphere	35	25	10	100	4
		Σ 50			Σ 8

$\chi^2 = 8$

(c) Degrees of freedom = 1 (2-1)
The critical value of χ^2 at $P = 0.05$ and at d.f.= 1 is 3.84. χ^2calc. > than the critical value (8 > 3.84).

(d) Reject H$_0$: The data are strongly in favour of H$_A$. Woodlice show significant preference for humid conditions over dry habitat conditions.
Note: When dealing with only two categories (i.e. d.f. = 1) **Yate's correction** formula should be used:
$\chi^2 = \Sigma ((O-E) - 0.5)^2 /E$
Using on this formula, $\chi^2 = 7.22$. This is still greater than the critical value so H$_0$ is rejected.

236. Investigating Distribution and Abundance
(page 318)

1.

Tree log	Distance from tree log (m)			
	0	1.5	2.5	3.5
1	22	23	5	3
2	17	8	6	5
3	17	14	10	5
4	6	9	3	8
5	18	13	18	15
6	21	20	15	3

2. Chi-squared is a statistical test to determine the significance of departures from an expected result (in this case that there would be no difference in the number of millipedes with distance from the log). Chi-squared can be used on this data because the data are counts (not measures or calculated values) and the counts can be tested against departures from the expected result (of no difference with distance).

3. Null hypothesis: The distance from the log has no effect on the density of millipedes in the leaf litter.

Alternative hypothesis: The distance from the log has an effect on the density of millipedes in the leaf litter.

4.

Distance (m)	O	E	O-E	(O-E)^2	(O-E)^2/E
0	101	71	30	900	12.7
1.5	87	71	16	256	3.6
2.5	57	71	-14	196	2.7
3.5	39	71	-32	1024	14.4
				Σ (O-E)^2/E	33.4

5. Chi-squared is very large for this test and as such the null hypothesis can be rejected in favour of the alternative hypothesis.

6. The results of the investigation significantly show that fallen logs have an effect on the distribution of millipedes in that the number of millipedes decreases with increasing distance from the log. This makes sense in relation to how millipedes live. Millipedes do not have a waterproof cuticle and thus lose water easily. Fallen logs tend to be moist underneath with an abundance of leaf litter and rotting wood, and would provide an ideal habitat for millipedes.

237. Transect Sampling (page 320)

1. (a) With belt transects of 10 m or more, sampling and analysis using this method is very time consuming and labour intensive.
(b) Line transects may not be representative of the community. There may be species which are present but which do not touch the line and are not recorded.
(c) Belt transects use a wider strip along the study area so there is less chance that a species will not be recorded.
(d) Situations involving highly mobile organisms.

2. Decrease the sampling interval. If no more species are detected and the trends along the transect remain the same, then the sampling interval was adequate.

3.

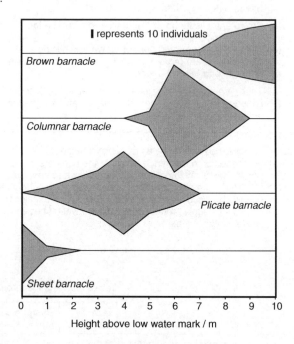

238. Qualitative Practical Work: Seaweed Zonation
(page 322)

1. (a) Percentage cover of each seaweed species.
(b) Seaweed vigour and degree of dessication.

2. Column graph as below:

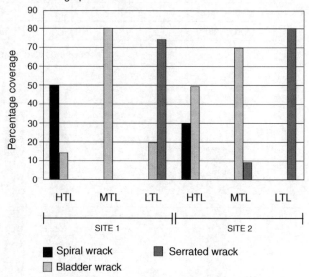

3. Spiral wrack is the most tolerant of long exposure periods, where it grows vigorously despite showing some evidence of desiccation. Bladder wrack grows vigorously throughout the

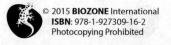

midlittoral and is relatively tolerant of exposure, only showing signs of desiccation higher on the shore where exposure times are longer. Serrated wrack is intolerant of exposure and grows vigorously at the LTL but shows signs of desiccation above this and cannot compete with the more tolerant bladder wrack.

4. Quadrat position was staggered for the two sites to give a better indication of the extent of each species' distribution. The disadvantage is that the sites cannot be directly compared.

239. Mark and Recapture Sampling (page 323)

1. Results will vary from group to group for this practical. The actual results are not important, but it should serve as a useful vehicle for discussion of such things as sample size, variation in results between groups, and whether the method is a reliable way to estimate the size of a larger unknown group. Discussion could centre around what factors could be altered to make it a more reliable method (e.g. larger sample size, degree of mixing, increasing number of samples taken).

2. Trout in Norwegian lake:
   Size of 1st sample: 109
   Size of 2nd sample: 177
   No. marked in 2nd sample: 57
   Estimated total population: 109 x 177 ÷ 57 = 338.5

3. (a) Some marked animals may die.
   (b) Not enough time for thorough mixing of marked and unmarked animals.

4. (a) and (b) in any order (any two of):
   – Marking does not affect their survival.
   – Marked & unmarked animals are captured randomly.
   – Marks are not lost.
   – The animals are not territorial (must mix back into the population after release).

5. (a) Any animal that cannot move or is highly territorial (e.g. barnacle, tube worm, many mammals).
   (b) Unable to mix with unmarked portion of the population. Recapture at the same location would simply sample the same animals again.

6. (a)-(c) in any order:
   – Banding: leg bands of different colour on birds.
   – Tags: crayfish shell, fish skin, mammal ears.
   – Paint/dye used to paint markings in shell/fur.

7. The scientists obtain information on fish growth to establish the relationship between age and growth. This will help manage the population to prevent overfishing. Tracking also helps to map breeding grounds and migrations so that fish can be protected at critical times in their life histories. In addition to these data, researchers will find out more about the general biology of the cod (e.g. data on feeding), which will help in the management and recovery of the fish stock.

240. Indirect Sampling (page 325)

1. (a) and (b) any of: Calls, tracks, markings on vegetation, scat.

2. (a) Information could be gathered on the distribution of hedgehogs, population size (from the number of tracks at different locations), and their habitat quality (from the location and habitat assessment).
   (b) This information will assist in determining the size of hedgehog populations in particular areas of the UK and whether they have the resources necessary for their long-term survival.

241 Sampling Using Radio-tracking (page 326)

1. Any of:
   – Recording the extent of their home range and the types of habitats they are using.
   – Recording dispersal after release into a new area (e.g. offshore island).
   – Recording the areas they are using (e.g. for feeding) which may be outside of the protected area they are living in (bats are a good example of this).

– Recording activity in relation to weather conditions and time of day (for some species, the accuracy of a population census depends on recording the animals at appropriate times).
– Monitoring migratory routes so that the species can be protected during their migration.
– Monitoring physiological state and learning more about the species biology.

2. In order to control pests effectively, it is useful to know the speed and extent of their dispersal and to understand the habitats they are using. Once habitat use in particular is accurately identified, these areas can be targeted for pest control. Knowing speed of spread enables control plans to be implemented that account for dispersal of the pest.

3. Marine animals are traditionally difficult to track because of the distance they travel and the vast expanse of the ocean. Radio-tracking, using satellites to detect the signal from the transmitter, has helped us to measure the distances covered by marine animals and the habitat they live in. In the case of the great white shark, data was provided on swimming speed and direction and showed that these animals do indeed undertake long migrations. This can help understanding of how these animals navigate. Radio-tracking can also provide information on nesting and breeding sites.

242. Chapter Review (page 327)

No model answer. Summary is the student's own.

243. KEY TERMS: Did You Get It? (page 328)

1. abundance (H), belt transect (F), carbon cycle (G), consumer (D), distribution (K), ecological pyramid (N), food chain (I), food web (E), line transect (A), mark and recapture (M), primary succession (L), quadrat (C), secondary succession (J), trophic level (B)

2. (a) Energy flows through the system and is lost as heat. Minerals cycle between organisms and the mineral nutrient pool.
   (b) Respiration

3. Producer → 1° consumer (herbivore) → 2° consumer (1° carnivore) → 3° consumer (2° carnivore)

244. Features of Populations (page 330)

1. (a) One of the following:
   Population growth rate: If this increases (or decreases) from one time interval to the next, it indicates that the population is probably also increasing (or decreasing). **Note**: The intrinsic rate of population increase (r_{max}) should be distinguished from population growth rates that account for the increasing number of individuals in the population (rN). The intrinsic population growth rate is a characteristic value for each species but rN can increase rapidly as more and more individuals add to the population increase.
   Total abundance: If this increases (or decreases) from one time interval to the next, it indicates that the population is also increasing (or decreasing).
   Mortality: If this is increasing from one time interval to the next, it indicates that the population may be decreasing (you must also account for other sources of population change).
   Birth rate & population fertility: If these increase from one time interval to the next, they indicate that the population may be increasing (you must also account for other sources of population change).
   Age structure: A population dominated by young individuals is usually increasing. A population dominated by old (especially post-reproductive) individuals is usually decreasing.
   (b) One of the following:
   Distribution: A very clumped distribution may indicate that only some parts of the environment are suitable for supporting individuals.
   Population growth and birth rates: If these are low or

declining it may indicate an inability of the environment to support the population density.

Mortality: If this are very high or increasing it *may* indicate an inability of the environment to support the present population density.

2. (a) Measurable attributes: Density, distribution, total abundance, sex ratios, migration (sometimes difficult). In some cases, depending on the organism, also age structure and population fertility.

(b) **Calculated attributes**: Population growth rate, birth rate (natality) and death rate (mortality).

3. (a) Population sampling of an endangered species allows us to determine (any of): If population is growing and how fast; the population's age and sex structure (i.e. is it dominated by young or old, non-reproductive, individuals); population abundance, density, and distribution in different areas (habitat preference and suitability); sources of mortality (predation, disease, starvation etc.); population fertility. This information allows informed decisions to be made about the population's management.

(b) Population sampling of a managed fish species allows us to determine the population growth rate. This is critical to establishing the level of fishing that can be supported by the population (the sustainable harvest) without irreversible population decline. The growth rate is calculated taking into account population abundance, and birth and death rates. Sustainable harvest can be built into the equation as one of the (controllable) sources of mortality.

245. The Carrying Capacity of an Ecosystem (page 331)

1. The carrying capacity is the maximum number of individuals of a particular species that an environment can support indefinitely.

2. The carrying capacity is set by the resources it can provide and these are limited. If a population increases above the carrying capacity, there will be insufficient resources to sustain it, and the population will decrease (e.g. through deaths) to a level that can be supported by the available resources.

3. (a) Food and space have been reduced.
   (b) Available water (and consequently food) are reduced due to the drought.
   (c) Water is more available.

246. A Case Study in Carrying Capacity (page 332)

1. Wolves were introduced to control the black-tailed deer, which were overgrazing the land.

2. (a) Factors causing the result included:
   – Coronation Island was too small to sustain both deer and wolf populations.
   – The deer couldn't hide from the wolves so could be reduced to very low numbers.
   – Reproductive rates of deer could have been low because of poor forage, so the population could not withstand predation.
   – There were no other prey so no opportunity for prey switching when deer became scarce.
   (b) The carrying capacity of Coronation Island is too low to support viable (sustainable) populations of a large predator (wolf) and its prey (deer).

247. The Rise and Fall of Human Populations
   (page 333)

1. The trend is of continual (close to exponential) growth in the human population.

2. The human population has grown because of increased crop yields and better medical treatment. This has led to a higher standard of living, better nutrition, and a lower mortality rate.

3. Local resources at Tikal and Easter Island were both used to support population growth. When these resources were over exploited, the populations crashed and the lands were abandoned. The early history of these examples tends to

mirror what appears to be currently happening on a global scale. This helps us understand the effects of depleted resources on populations whose livelihoods are based on those resources and what can be done to prevent similar events happening again.

248. Species Interactions (page 334)

1. (a) Mutualism: Domesticated animals (e.g. dogs and cats in western culture, work horses) and plants not grown for consumption.

(b) Exploitation: Using plants and animals for food source, skins/pelts for clothing, timber and other plant products for shelter and building materials.

(c) Competition: Invertebrate pests and some fungi feeding on our crops (e.g. insects such as aphids, locusts, caterpillars; slugs, snails, mildew, rusts).

2. (a) Acacia produces toxic alkaloids in response to browsing.
   (b) This response makes the giraffe move on to another plant before it removes too much of the acacia's foliage

249. Interpreting Predator-Prey Relationships
   (page 335)

1. (a) Peak numbers of woolly aphids and ladybird marked on graph (below).

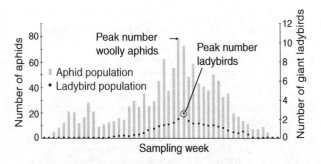

(b) No, they are slightly offset (ladybirds lag).
(c) Giant ladybirds feed only on woolly aphids, so ladybird numbers can only increase if there is enough food (woolly aphids) to sustain population growth. Giant ladybird numbers will respond to the woolly aphid numbers and slightly lag behind.

2. (a) Positive.
   (b) Giant ladybird numbers follow the trend for woolly aphid numbers. When woolly aphid numbers are increasing, the giant ladybird numbers increase. As woolly aphid numbers decrease so do the giant ladybird numbers.

3. (a) Usually between about 3 and 7 years (especially for pronounced peaks), although sometimes as great as a full 10 year cycle. **Explanatory note**: The peaks often appear to be superimposed or the lynx peaks appear to be ahead of the hare peaks. Remember that the lynx are responding to the earlier peaks in hare abundance.

(b) The lag is the result of the time it takes for the predator to respond (through increased births) to increases in food supply. **Explanatory note**: Lynx are top predators, with longer reproductive times and generation times than hares. When the hare populations increase there is a considerable lag before this increase in available food is translated into higher population growth rates in lynx. Likewise, a fall in hare numbers takes some time to be registered by a decline in lynx population growth rate.

4. Hares are the main food item for lynx in this system and there is little opportunity for prey switching. The lynx cycles follow those of the hares closely with a similar periodicity.

5. (a) When the supply of palatable food declines, birth rates decline (adults are less well nourished and litters are smaller) and the mortality rate increases (more deaths due to starvation and disease as a result of malnutrition). Note: Population growth rates depend on both birth and death rates: $(r = b - d)$. When natality declines and mortality increases, r becomes negative and the

population declines.

(b) High mortality (deaths) can be sustained by species such as rodents and lagomorphs as long as they can maintain their intrinsically high birth rates. Declines in palatable food adversely affects their ability to do this.

6. Because the system is totally enclosed, the predators do not have any other prey to eat when prey numbers get low. Also prey has nowhere to hide. Eventually all the prey are eaten and the predators will starve (system collapses).

250. Intraspecific Competition (page 337)

1. (a) Individual growth rate: Intraspecific competition may reduce individual growth rate when there are insufficient resources for all individuals. Examples: tadpoles, *Daphnia*, many mammals with large litters. Explanatory note: Individuals compete for limited resources and growth is limited in those that do not get access to sufficient food.

(b) Population growth rate: Intraspecific competition reduces population growth rate. Examples as above. Explanatory note: Competition intensifies with increasing population size and, at carrying capacity, the rate of population increase slows to zero.

(c) Final population size: Intraspecific competition will limit population size to a level that can be supported by the carrying capacity of the environment. Note: In territorial species, this will be determined by the number of suitable territories that can be supported.

2. (a) They reduce their individual growth rate and take longer to reach the size for metamorphosis.

(b) Density dependent.

(c) The results of this tank experiment are unlikely to represent a real situation in that the tank tadpoles are not subject to normal sources of mortality and there is no indication of long term survivability (of the growth retarded tadpoles). Note: At high densities, many tadpoles would fail to reproduce and this would naturally limit population growth (and size) in the longer term.

3. Reduce intensity of intraspecific competition by:

(a) Establishing hierarchies within a social group to give orderly access to resources.

(b) Establishing territories to defend the resource within a specified area.

4. (a) Carrying capacity might decline as a result of unfavourable climatic events (drought, flood etc.) or loss of a major primary producer (plant species).

(b) Final population size would be smaller (relative to what it was when carrying capacity was higher).

5. Territoriality is a common consequence of intraspecific competition in mammals and birds. In any habitat, resources are limited and only those with sufficient resources will be able to breed. This is especially the case with mammals and birds, where the costs of reproduction to the individual are high relative to some other taxa. Even though energy must be used in establishing and maintaining a territory, territoriality is energy efficient in the longer term because it gives the breeding pair relatively unchallenged access to resources. As is shown in the territory maps of golden eagles and great tits, territories space individuals apart and reduce intraspecific interactions. The size of the territory is related to the resources available within the defended area; larger territories are required when resources are poorer or widely dispersed. As is shown by the great tit example, when territory owners are removed, their areas are quickly occupied by birds previously displaced by competition.

251. Interspecific Competition (page 339)

1. The two species have similar niche requirements (similar habitats and foods). Red squirrels once occupied a much larger range than currently. This range has contracted steadily since the introduction of the greys. The circumstantial evidence points to the reds being displaced by the greys.

2. The greys have not completely displaced the reds. In areas of suitable coniferous habitat, the reds have maintained their numbers. In some places the two species coexist. **Note:** It has

been suggested that the reds are primarily coniferous dwellers and extended their range into deciduous woodland habitat in the absence of competition.

3. Habitat management allows more effective long term population management *in-situ* (preferable because the genetic diversity of species is generally maintained better in the wild). Reds clearly can hold their own in competition with greys, provided they have sufficient resources. **Enhancing the habitat** preferred by the reds (through preservation and tree planting), assists their success. Providing **extra suitable food plants** also enables the reds to increase their breeding success and maintain their weight through winter (thus entering the breeding season in better condition).

4. Other conservation strategies could include (any of): Captive breeding and release of reds into areas where they have been displaced, control/cull of grey squirrels (particularly in habitats suitable for reds), transfer of reds from regions where populations are successful to other regions of suitable habitat, supplementary feeding prior to the breeding season, public education to encourage red squirrels over greys.

5. (a) A represents the **realised niche** of *Chthamalus*.

(b) When *Balanus* is removed from the lower shore, the range of *Chthamalus* extends into areas previously occupied by the *Balanus*; *Balanus* normally excludes *Chthamalus* from the lower shore.

252. Conservation and Sustainability (page 341)

1. Conservation refers to the management of a resource so that it is maintained into the future. The resource may be a living or mineral system and may focus on the efficient use of a non-renewable resource or the managed use of a living system. Sustainability refers to the idea of using resources within the capacity of the environment and the eventual replacement of what has been used. It can be viewed as a subset of conservation, mainly focussing on living systems.

2. Resource conservation is the efficient use of resources so that stocks remain available into the future. This means not wasting non-renewable resources (e.g. oil) and making sure renewable resources can be replenished at the same (or greater) rate as they are used (e.g. fish stocks).

3. Society and the economy are important in conservation because a strong economy and a stable, equitable society contribute to higher employment, better living standards, and a higher level of education. These in turn promote sound infrastructure (e.g. sewage disposal), increase awareness of the environment and resource use, and promote economic decisions that support conservation aims. If society is disrupted, e.g. by conflict, and the economy is weak, resources will be exploited to survive.

253. Sustainable Forestry (page 342)

1. (a) Coppicing is a low-impact method of producing wood for harvest, which preserves a rich diversity of woodland species and is sustainable in the long term. However, it is a low volume method and the timber is not suitable for all uses. It is also skilled and labour intensive work and, if not carried out properly, has detrimental effects on diversity and forest structure.

(b) Strip cutting harvests a forest in strips and has the advantage that it produces relatively high volumes of timber suitable for a wide range of uses while leaving enough border forest to enable rapid recovery of cleared land. It is also a low effort for return method and has a relatively low impact on the environment and on biodiversity. Most disadvantages come from the infrastructure required to carry out the forestry (roads etc) and the constraint of regeneration time (so for slow growing species it is not suitable).

(c) Clear cutting is a high volume method with significant detrimental impacts on the environment (e.g. high soil erosion, habitat loss, reduced biodiversity). The forest requires replanting and, if suitable at all, clear cutting should be restricted to fast growing plantation forests.

(d) Selection logging is a medium volume supplier of timber,

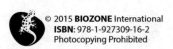

but causes a moderate amount of environmental damage, which depends partly on how much infrastructure and machinery are associated with the timber extraction. Effects on biodiversity are usually minimal, and can be sustainable if properly managed to retain the original forest composition.

2. (a) Commercial plantations: Clear cutting.
   (b) Traditional woodland: Coppicing.
   (c) Second growth: Strip cutting or selective logging.

3. The student's own opinion is important here and should be qualified. Given unlimited resources, coppicing provides long term sustainability, with volume supplied from a mix of selective logging and strip cutting in second growth and plantation forests. Logging of old growth forests should never be considered sustainable.

4. Properly coppiced woodlands provide a regular timber supply and maintain an open canopy that encourages a rich understorey and faunal diversity. If a previously coppiced woodland is allowed to deteriorate without management, it becomes tall and overshaded, yet lacking the characteristics of an old growth forest. Biodiversity declines markedly. These are strong arguments for managing coppiced lands as a long term resource.

254. Sustainable Fishing (page 344)

1. Without accurate estimates of age, population size and growth rate it is impossible to calculate an accurate MSY. Incorrect calculation of the MSY may lead to over fishing and the collapse of the fishery, or to under fishing with not enough fish being landed to create a viable economic resource.

2. (a) Overestimating the population size leads to overestimating replenishment rate and the size of the sustainable catch.
   (b) Overestimating the growth rate leads to overestimating the size of the catch that can be landed due to the assumption the population will quickly recover its loses.
   (c) This scenario could lead to the MSY being set too low due to the assumption that the population ages and replaces its losses slowly. It may also lead to the assumption that the population is close to collapse.

3. The statement is correct in that the population can only be harvested at the MSY if the population growth rate remains stable. If the rate drops but the MSY remains the same then each season a greater proportion of the population will be taken. For example, a population of 100 has 40 taken each season (leaving 60). If a bad season sees the population recover to only 90 before the next harvest of 40 the population will be reduced to 50. A second bad season may see a further reduction. Harvesting at the MSY leaves the population vulnerable to changes in its population growth. Because of this, quotas are normally set below the MSY.

4. (a) Total catch rate has declined and is now nearly 300 000 tonnes less than during peak harvests in the 1970s. Mortality increased to a peak around 1990-2000 but has steadily declined since then. Spawning and recruitment rates have both declined dramatically. Spawning stock biomass has recovered slightly since 2005.
   (b) There will be little effect on stock recovery. This measure will only slow its decline, rather than increase numbers. This is because the current estimated maximum mortality rate is 0.2, lower than the fisheries target of 0.4.

255. Managing Environmental Resources (page 346)

1. Logging provides new land for crops and also provides money or resources from the sale or use of the timber produced.

2. Situations include:
   – wildlife is using land that could be used for growing food or providing other resources such as timber.
   – Wildlife damages property and crops - it's better to remove the wildlife
   – There is no monetary value in living animals, but they can be sold as trophies etc.

3. Without public involvement, the benefits of resource management are not understood by the public. Thus the public continue to regard the efforts as a waste of time and money

and retain the attitude that money should be directed to other projects (food, crops, housing) .

4. (a) The conservancies are areas of land owned by a collective. The land is used for conservation and tourism and payments to the owners are made for use of the land.
   (b) The conservancies have reduced conflict by reducing the amount of farming on the land (so there is little crop destruction or damage to equipment). The conservancies increase controls over land use so it is less likely that wildlife and humans will have contact in conflicting ways.

256. Controlling Human Impact (page 348)

1. Ecotourism can reduce human impact by controlling access to sensitive areas. This can occur by way of regulation, with tourists or tourism operators applying for permits to visit certain areas. The permit can be linked to ensuring tourists and operators behave in ways that are appropriate to the environment. In this way, land is protected for tourists to visit, and the tourists are prevented from damaging environmentally sensitive land. Income is generated without damage to the land, reducing the need or desire to use the land for other human activities (e.g. farming).

2. **Benefits of ecotourism**:
   – Greater economic activity and better economic growth as a result of more jobs in the tourist industry.
   – Greater local and global environmental awareness.
   – Development of support services for conservation.
   Disadvantages of ecotourism:
   – Environmental disturbance by tourists.
   – Increase in rubbish, and strain on resources in providing tourist services.
   – Diversion of tourist dollars from the local economy.
   – Risks of alien species invading with more sea traffic.
   – Restrictions on traditional income sources, e.g. fishing.

3. (a) Increased tourist traffic increases the risks of habitat disturbance and may directly threaten some species if they are in vulnerable areas.
   (b) A higher local population puts greater pressure on park boundaries and increases the risks associated with pollution and rubbish disposal, both of which directly and indirectly affect flora and fauna. Fish stocks may benefit though as a result of tighter regulations on local fishing.
   (c) Improvements in National Park services have enabled the funding of restoration projects on a number of islands, including the removal of feral pigs and goats. This has directly benefited native biota, allowing vegetation regeneration and better survival of native animal species,
   (d) Tourism in the Galápagos is highly restricted, with guides accompanying all tourist excursions. Their input has helped to protect the native species from tourist pressure and made people more environmentally aware, so they think carefully about the impact of their activities. Education at the local level helps people to understand how they can benefit (environmentally and economically) from conservation of the islands. These aspects help to raise the profile of the environment and the biota benefit as a consequence of that.

257. Chapter Review (page 350)

No model answer. Summary is the student's own.

258. KEY TERMS: Did You Get It? (page 351)

1. (a) Approximately 6000 individuals.
   (b) Population was entering a phase of exponential growth.
   (c) The population had crashed to a low point.
   (d) The population had exceeded carrying capacity by a large amount and would have run out of resources. Many individuals would have died and population growth would have fallen dramatically.

2. biodiversity (K), carrying capacity (H), competition (C), conservation (L), distribution (J), interspecific competition (I), intraspecific competition (G), maximum sustainable yield (A), mortality (D), natality (E), population size (N), predator (B), prey (F), sustainable (M)

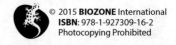
© 2015 **BIOZONE** International
ISBN: 978-1-927309-16-2
Photocopying Prohibited